How To Make the OSHA—1970 Work For You

How To Make the OSHA—1970 Work For You

Handbook of the Williams-Steiger Occupational Safety and Health Administration

DAVID R. SHOWALTER
President
Human Resources Conservancy
Tacoma, Washington

ann arbor science PUBLISHERS INC.
P.O. BOX 1425 • ANN ARBOR, MICHIGAN 48106

221986

CONTENTS

CHAPTER ONE
Introduction

This book is intended for both management and employee. It has direct application to president, union member and worker alike, and it can be immeasurably helpful in meeting the requirements of an Act (Federal and state) which, necessary though it may be, still remains maligned, criticized and misunderstood by management, labor, the safety professional (who ought to know better) and even the worker for whom it was intended.

Few people seem to recognize the potential (let alone the merit) of its basic employee relations aspect. If such recognition is granted it is accorded a negative rather than positive emphasis.

Many people still argue about its wordage. The Act, in plain truth, is about safety, not semantics. It seeks to establish a safe and healthful workplace for all workers.

Although not stated in the following way, the objective of the Williams-Steiger bill is fourfold.

(1) to reduce the number of fatalities occurring annually in the American workplace

(2) to reduce the number, severity and cost of job-related injuries and health problems

(3) to help establish the security and well-being of those who do the job for us

(4) to reduce profit-loss and increase profit-potential for business and industry.

That is an intelligent and practical assessment of what the Act really is and is a 4-point objective rather difficult, impractical, if not indeed downright unintelligent, to argue with.

The validity of the fourth point is substantiated by the insurance industry again and again, year after year. Accidents are phenomenally costly and are paid for from the profit side of the ledger— not the production side. As a matter of simple fact it is more accurate to say that in the end it is the consumer who really pays for industrial fatalities and injuries.

Assistant Secretary of Labor, George C. Guenther, the first federal department head to be charged with the new responsibility contained in the Act, stated, that *protectivity*—a new concept in the safe and healthful work place laws—makes the gains of *productivity* possible. The point is well made. Whether or not "protectivity" becomes equal to "productivity" as an integral and essential part of profit-making for American business and industry remains to be seen.

The truth, nonetheless, is incontestable. With few exceptions, profit-making has never yet considered loss control, risk management, accident prevention, safety—however, it is termed—as anything other than part of production and of negative, minimum, or no importance if it interfered in any way with maximum production.

What the Assistant Secretary of Labor was suggesting and what the Act may bring into sharp focus is that safety as such is a separate and important issue; it is a part of the profit-making or profit-losing process; it is of equal importance with production, sales and merchandising, advertising and promotion, public and community relations, and when successfully managed helps make the whole process that much more profitable.

CHAPTER TWO
Who's on First?

As president, owner, executive officer, by whatever title (if you are the individual where the buck stops passing) you will need to be involved with the Act (Federal and state), at least to the point where you know what it is, how it applies to you, and generally what needs to be done about it. It is embarrassing, not to mention impractical, unprofitable and unintelligent, to find your company on the short end of the "inspection stick," cited with several alleged violations and fined hundreds or thousands of dollars because somebody didn't get the message.

It has happened. As a very busy, involved and active chief executive of a company faced with all the problems and details that successful management requires, you would find the above circumstance very irritating indeed.

The alleged violations, however, had their origin with you. To avoid such a situation, you must first read the Act. Next you need to assign the full responsibility for it to some individual. He should then always report directly to you. Then you need to act. Do something about implementing the Act. Some suggestions are made in the following pages.

Don't think, or let anyone else think, that the Act will just go away or that it doesn't apply to you. It won't go away. The enactment of a law by the Congress of these United States of America takes some doing in the first place. Once enacted it doesn't rescind or even amend too easily.

Similar enabling Acts by 50 state legislatures, providing states with the administration of their own safety and health regulatory procedures, bring it even closer to home on a local functioning level. This further emphasizes the fact that the Act(s) is/are here to stay. And, while nobody can deny the ameliorating effect that political or vested interest pressures exert on any legislation, there is, in this case, a very capable, interested and vocal proponent and guardian of it—organized labor.

The Act applies to you if you have one or more employees working for you.

It has a more intensified, more comprehensive application if your business falls within any designation of *target industry*—those industries with the highest accident frequency rates. The first of these are longshoring, meat and meat packing, wood products, sheet metal and roofing, and mobile home construction.

One of OSHA's first approaches within the federal administration of the Act was to inspect these five target industries. What the next five will be is anybody's guess, but a look at the U. S. Department of Labor's statistical analysis of accidents by industry is a good indication. A "Target Health Hazards" program was established focusing on five toxic substances which affect workplaces—asbestos, cotton dust, silica, lead and carbon monoxide. OSHA inspection priorities included both the new program and industrial hygiene inspections carried out in thousands of workplaces.

In the event of a job-related fatality or an accident hospitalizing five or more workers, a CSHO (Compliance Safety and Health Officer) is on the spot to make an investigation.

The program also provides for an almost immediate investigation of an employee request for an inspection of a workplace considered to be unsafe or unhealthful, provided that the "request" is stated with "reasonable particularity," and is basically valid. The possibility that it may be the object of an inspection by virtue of the "random sampling" part of the inspection program, used along with the "target industry" approach, can not be overlooked by any business.

The Act (Federal and state) in its voluntary compliance principle, operates similarly to IRS. There are not now, nor will there ever be, enough compliance officers to annually inspect all business establishments affected by the Act. However, the possibility, even the probability, of inspection always exists. The fines and penalties attached to failure to comply with the standards are a healthy deterrent factor.

Another deterrent, although not given much recognition at this point, is the "interest" pressure from various groups. Trade association peer groups, who are not only affected and conforming but in many cases leading the way, are apt to take a dim view of any recalcitrant individual member who makes trouble for himself and other members as well. Unions, already dissatisfied with the Act in many ways and particularly critical of the relinquishment of federal administration of the national legislation to state enacted legislation and subsequent administration, are certain to watch the progress, or lack of it, closely. With the passage of time, as the Act becomes better known, public and citizen interest can also become critical.

Employers must maintain records of each job-related accident or illness. These records must be available for inspection purposes. A sampling from various selected industries goes to Washington, D.C. for study, analysis and evaluation. One annual form and summary must be posted for all employees to see. A system of fines and penalties has been devised as a deterrent measure for business that may tend to disregard the compliance specifications of the Act.

One far-reaching application and implication of the Act is that it involves the individual worker in several interesting aspects. The employee has both a right and a responsibility. He, or employee representative, can "request" an inspection, and do so with anonymous immunity. In the present Williams-Steiger Act, he cannot be cited or fined. Employees must be represented on all inspection tours and resultant conferences with management by a worker of their choice. Employees have "due recourse" or "due process" similar to employers. Employees can challenge the Secretary's decision if they feel his action is inimical or harmful to them.

Many employers become so involved in the employee rights aspect of the Act that they overlook and don't believe several positive factors in their favor. One of these is the responsibility of the employee. He must "comply with the safety and health standards applicable to the individual workplace." While an employer is charged and faced with the responsibility of enforcing a particular regulation, he does not have to keep an employee who is in constant violation of the employee responsibility. Such an employee can be discharged.

Also there is no collective bargaining issue here unless the Act, its Congressional intent, meaning, and specific terminology are completely subverted. Neither the employer, the employee, or the union, can abrogate their separate and collective responsibility under the terms of the Act. The employer's responsibility is plainly and simply stated, and the employee's responsibility is plainly and simply stated. The union, as the bargaining agent or representative of the employee in the middle between employer and employee, is faced with consideration of both sides of the coin.

As a matter of observable fact, the Act involves everybody who *is* involved about as totally and responsibly as can be set down on paper. Employers, employees and unions alike are bound together in this package in a fashion where no one member of this triumvirate can accuse the other without first tending to its own responsibility.

A union, for example, cannot argue the case of an employee proven to be in violation of a standard, and proven to have been given a fair and equitable opportunity to mend his ways, and failing that discharged by the employer. It cannot argue the case, that is, without defeating its own cause—the Act itself.

It is important, then, for the executive officer who may go no farther than these introductory pages to be sure that one individual, preferably a safety director, is responsible for the Act and to see that a safety committee is organized to help get the job done. The safety committee must understand what its functions and responsibilities are as they relate directly to the Act. It must be recognized that an already established safety committee, or safety director, may tend to follow already established lines of procedure and action. They must be made to see the fallacy of that immediately.

In all probability they will need to make a 180-degree turn. They should focus on the Williams-Steiger Occupational Safety and Health Act of 1970 and its corresponding state legislation. Practically speaking that is where all the industrial safety and health action is and will be.

Philosophically speaking, the Act is an excellent base for an effective and in many ways profitable and comprehensive safety and health program—a comparatively new experience for great numbers of business, industry and political subdivisions.

A last word of explanation. It is difficult, if not almost impossible, to write a definitive handbook or guideline on an Act that has two bases—federal and state. There are bound to be some discrepancies and differences. If, however, you and your personnel use the parent Williams-Steiger Occupational Safety and Health Act of 1970 as your informational source and specific guideline, you can be certain that your state Act will basically parallel OSHA—1970.

State Acts must be at least as effective. State administration of the program is monitored for three years by the Occupational Safety and Health Administration. If the state plan is ineffectual it can be removed and the federal plan reinstated. States, without exception, have developed their own plans with federal funds allocated to them for that purpose. The cost of administration of state programs is supported by the federal government on a 50-50 matching fund basis. All of it, plainly stated, is a kind of covert control mechanism difficult to ignore.

Although state Acts and plans may vary somewhat, if you substitute the state agency, director, compliance officer and due process for the federal terminology you will have a basic understanding of the Act.

CHAPTER THREE
Readthrough of the Act
– Salient Points

1. Employer "shall" provide a safe and healthful workplace for all employees.

2. Employer "shall" comply with safety and health standards.

3. Employee "shall" comply with safety and health standards.

4. "Standards" were issued 29 May, 1971, Federal Register, compiled from all federal contracts Acts, ANSI and NFPA standards—known as consensus standards. Changes, new standards, clarifications are constantly being made, issued and formulated. All are noted and brought up to date via the Federal Register, and via publication from OSHA when available.

5. Compliance inspections will be made by Federal compliance officers, by state inspectors deputized and trained as Federal Compliance officers, and, when state plan is in effect, by state compliance officers.

6. Citations will be issued on an "alleged" basis, if an employer or an employee is found in "violation" of any one of the standards applicable.

7. Employer can be assessed fines and penalties:

A. $1,000 for a serious violation.

B. $1,000 a day for each day, each violation, past the specified abatement period.

C. $10,000 for "failure to exercise reasonable diligence" in detecting violations or willfully or repeatedly ignoring any of the obligations, standards, rules, orders or regulations of the Act.

D. $10,000, six months in prison, or both for willful violations of any standard, rule, regulation or order that causes death to any employee.

E. $20,000, one year in prison or both for subsequent willful violation that causes death.

F. $10,000 for false statement, representation or certification in any document, file or record maintained.

G. $1,000 or six months or both for advance notice of inspection without authorization (e.g., any warning ahead of time or notification of inspection by an unauthorized source).

H. $1,000 each violation of posting requirements.

I. $5,000-$10,000 and, or 3-10 years in prison for killing, assaulting or resisting certain Federal law enforcement officers in performance of officers in performance of official duties.

All fines are paid to the U. S. Secretary of Labor for deposit into U. S. Treasury, and accrue to the United States.

Note: The above are maximum. Fines can be, and frequently are minimal ($50.00, $100.00, etc.).

8. Reduction of fines (Fines can be reduced as much as 75% for nonserious violations, and 50% for both nonserious and serious violations.

Reductions are awarded on the basis of good faith, employer's attitude and evidence of willingness to improve safety performance, history of the employer, and size of the business.

9. Citations are issued for:

A. *Imminent Danger.* "Any conditions or practices in any place of employment which are such that a danger exists which could reasonably be expected to cause death or serious physical harm immediately or before the imminence of such danger can be eliminated through the enforcement procedures otherwise provided through this Act."

B. *Serious.* "If there is a substantial probability that death or physical harm could result from a condition which exists, or from one or more practice, means, methods, or processes which have been adopted, or are in use."

C. *Nonserious.* "A violation is not a serious one if an employer through the exercise of reasonable diligence, did not, or could not discover it."

D. *De Minimis.* "No direct or immediate relationship to safety or health." A notice that details the conditions and circumstances of the violation, and prescribes the means for correcting it.

Note: The citation, which forms the basis for subsequent enforcement proceedings, should describe "with particularity" the nature of the violation and should note the provision, standard, rule, regulation or order which has allegedly been violated. The citation should also fix a "reasonable" time period in which the employer must correct the violation.

10. Notice of penalty

Employer must be notified by *certified mail* within "reasonable time" after the termination of such inspection or investigation what the penalty is, if any, and that he has 15 working days after receipt of the notice within which to notify the Secretary if he wishes to contest the citation or proposed assessment of penalties.

The 15-day working period begins on the first working day after receipt of the notice. It does not include Saturdays, Sundays or Federal holidays.

If there is no contest within that 15-day period or no employee or employee rep files notice with the Secretary alleging that the time fixed in the citation for the abatement of violation is unreasonable, the citation and penalty are a final order and not subject to review.

11. Employer/employee/employee representative can appeal to Occupational Safety and Health Review Commission. If the employer wishes to contest a citation or proposed assessment of penalty, or if an employee or employee rep files notice alleging that the period of time for abatement of the violation is unreasonable, the Secretary must notify OSHRC, and the Commission must provide an opportunity for a hearing.

The Commission then issues an order, based on findings of fact, affirming, modifying or vacating the Secretary's citation or proposed penalty, or prescribing "other appropriate relief." The order becomes final 30 days after issue.

If an employer can demonstrate that he has tried, in good faith, to comply with the abatement requirements of the citation and that failure to comply is due to factors "beyond reasonable control" the Secretary after an opportunity for a hearing, shall issue an order affirming or modifying the abatement requirement in the citation. Affected employee representatives of affected employees shall be provided with an opportunity to participate as parties to the hearing.

12. Informal conference. Any employer or employee affected by a citation, notice of proposed penalty, or assessment of penalty, may request an informal conference with the Regional Administrator, or Solicitor, or the representative of either, to negotiate a re-inspection, or otherwise achieve a settlement of the issues. All parties may be represented by counsel. The conference does not serve as a stay of the 15-day notice of contest requirements.

13. The employer has further right of appeal to U. S. Court of Appeals. He can contest an order of the Occupational Safety and Health Review Commission by filing a petition with the U. S. Court of Appeals for the circuit in which the violation allegedly occurred, the circuit in which the employer has his principal office, or in the Court of Appeals for the District of Columbia.

14. Record keeping, Reporting. The record keeping began on 1 July, 1971, and will be prepared on a calendar year basis. Regulations require each employer covered by the Act to maintain three sets of records: (A) a log of all "recordable" (see below for definition) injuries and illnesses, (B) a supplementary record of illnesses and injuries, and (C) an annual summary.

A. Log of recordable injuries and illnesses (Form 100)

(1) Each employer shall maintain in each establishment a log of all recordable occupational injuries and illnesses for that establishment, except that under the circumstances described in paragraph 2 below, an employer may maintain the log of occupational injuries and illnesses at a place other than the establishment.

Each employer shall enter each recordable occupational injury and illness on the log as early as practicable but no later than 6 working days after receiving information that a recordable case has occurred.

For this purpose OSHA Form No. 100 or any private equivalent may be used. OSHA Form No. 100 or its equivalent shall be completed in the detail provided in the form and the instruction contained in OSHA Form No. 100. If an equivalent to OSHA Form No. 100 is used, such as a printout from data-processing equipment, the information shall be as readable and comprehensible to a person not familiar with the data-processing equipment as the OSHA Form No. 100 itself.

(2) Any employer may maintain the log of occupational injuries and illnesses at a place other than the establishment, or by means of data-processing equipment or both, under the following circumstances:

(a) There is available at the place where the log is maintained sufficient information to complete the log to a date within six working days after receiving information that a recordable case has occurred.

(b) A copy of the log, complete and current to a date within 45 calendar days, which reflects separately the illness and injury of that establishment, be available.

B. Supplementary Record (Form 101)

In addition to the log of occupational injuries and illnesses, each employer shall have available for inspection at each establishment within six working days, after receiving information that a recordable case has occurred, a supplementary record for each occupational injury or illness, for that establishment.

The record shall be completed in the detail prescribed in the instructions accompanying OSHA Form No. 101. Workmen's compensation, insurance, or other reports are acceptable alternative records if they contain the information required by OSHA Form No. 101. If no acceptable alternative record is maintained for other purposes, OSHA Form No. 101 shall be used, or the necessary information shall be otherwise maintained.

C. Annual summary (Form 102)

(1) Each employer shall compile an annual summary of occupational injuries and illnesses for each establishment. Each annual summary shall be based on the information contained in the log of occupational injuries and illnesses for the particular establishment. OSHA Form No. 102 shall be used for this purpose, and shall be completed in the form and detail as provided in the instructions contained therein.

(2) The summary shall be completed no later than one month after the close of each calendar year, beginning with the calendar year, 1971.

(3) Each employer, or the office or employee of the employer who supervises the preparation of the annual summary of occupational injuries and illnesses, shall certify that the annual summary is true and complete. The certification shall be accomplished by affixing the signature of the employer, or the officer or employee who supervises the preparation of the annual summary to the lower right hand corner of the annual summary, certifying that it is true and complete.

(4) Each employer shall post a copy of the establishment's summary in each establishment. The summary shall be posted no later than 1 February, and shall remain in place for 30 consecutive calendar days thereafter.

15. Recordable occupational injuries or illnesses: Those injuries or illnesses which result in fatalities, or lost workdays, and those which do not involve lost workdays but require transfer to another job, termination of employment, or medical treatment other than first aid are recordable. Cases involving loss of consciousness or restriction of work or motion, including any diagnosed occupational illnesses which are not reported to the employer, but are not classified as fatalities or lost workday cases are also included.

A. Medical treatment: treatment administered by a physician or registered professional personnel under standing orders of a physician.

B. First aid: one-time treatment and any follow-up visit for the purpose of observing minor scratches, cuts, bruises, splinters, and similar situations which do not ordinarily require medical care. Even when first aid is administered by a physician or registered professional personnel, it is not considered medical treatment.

C. Lost workdays: the total number of days, (not necessarily consecutive) following, but not including, the day of injury or illness that an employee was unable to perform all or any part of his normal assignment because of the job-related injury or illness.

D. Establishment: a single physical location where business is conducted, or where services or industrial operations are performed.

Records must be kept in each establishment for five years, following the end of the calendar year to which they apply. If ownership changes, the new owner is responsible for portion of year in which he assumed ownership. The previous records, however, must be kept for the time specified.

Records must be available for inspection and copying by Compliance Safety and Health Officers (CSHO), representatives of HEW, Bureau of Labor Statistics, and state compliance officers where state has been awarded jurisdiction over safety and health inspections or statistical compilations.

16. Reporting: Within 48 hours, employers must report to the nearest office of the Area Director:

A. occupational accidents or illnesses fatal to one or more employees.

B. occupational accidents or illnesses which result in the hospitalization of five or more employees.

The report may be oral or written but must detail the circumstances of the accident, the number of fatalities, and the extent of any injuries. The Area Director may then require any additional information he deems appropriate.

17. Falsification or failure to keep records or reports: **Whoever** knowingly makes any false statement, representation, or certification in any application, record, plan or other document filed or required to be maintained pursuant to this Act shall upon conviction be punished by a fine of not more than $10,000, or by imprisonment for not more than six months, or both.

Failure to maintain records or file reports required by this part, or in the details required by forms and instructions issued under this part, may result in the issuance of citations and assessment of penalties.

Any employer who wishes to maintain records in a manner different from that required by this part of the Act may submit a petition containing this information to the Regional Director of the Bureau of Labor Statistics wherein the establishment involved is located. The petition shall include:

(1) The name and address of the applicant.

(2) The address of the place or places of employment involved.

(3) Specification of the reasons relief is sought.

(4) A description of the different record keeping procedures proposed by the applicant.

(5) A statement that the applicant has informed his employees of the petition by giving a copy thereof to their authorized representative and by posting a statement giving a summary of the petition and by other appropriate means. A statement made pursuant to this shall be posted in each establishment. The applicant shall also state that he has informed his employees of their rights.

(6) In the event an employer has more than one establishment he shall submit a list of the states in which such establishments are located and the number of establishments in each such state. In the further event that certain of the employer's establishments would not be affected by the petition, the employer shall identify every establishment which would be affected by the petition and give the state in which they are located.

(7) Any employer with eight or less employees is only required to report (a) an occupational fatality, or (b) an injury resulting in multiple hospitalization.

18. Citation posting requirements: These must be prominently posted by the employer at or near the place where the violation occurred—a place where employees will see the notice. They must remain for three days or until the hazard is abated, whichever is later, or until the Commission issues a final order that the citation should be dismissed.

The employer may also post a notice in the same location stating that the citation is being contested before the Commission.

19. Employee rights and responsibilities

A. An employee or employee representative can "request" an inspection. This can be initiated by a telephone call to the Area Director, but ultimately it must be submitted in writing.

The request must state that the employee or employee representative believes that a "violation of safety or health standard exists that threatens physical harm or that imminent danger exists" in a place where work is performed. The notice must set forth with "reasonable particularity" the conditions for which the inspection is being requested. It must state also whether it concerns an imminent danger and what steps the employee or employee representative has taken to rectify the situation.

Although the notice to OSHA must be signed by either the employee or employee representative, the name or names of employees referred to therein will not appear in the copy of the notice or any report of information published pursuant thereto. The Area Director or Compliance Officer must provide the employer with a copy of the notice no later than the time of the inspection.

If the Secretary determines, as a result of the employee allegation there are reasonable grounds for an inspection, he shall initiate a special inspection as soon as practicable to determine whether such violation or danger exists. The inspection need not be limited to matters referred to in the request for an inspection. If the Secretary determines that grounds for such an investigation do not exist, he must so indicate to the employees or their representative.

In the course of such an inspection, or any inspection, employees can call the attention of the compliance officer to violations of any safety and health standards.

B. Employee representatives can accompany compliance officers on inspection tours of workplaces.

C. Employee representatives are to be included in the Compliance Officer's report to and conference with the employer after the inspection tour.

D. Employees may communicate with the Secretary in connection with any proceeding under the Act.

E. Employees may participate as parties to any hearing, contest any action of the Commission, or contest the period of time allowed for the abatement of a violation.

F. Employers must keep employees informed of their protections and obligations under the Act including the provisions of applicable standards.

G. The Act provides safeguards for employees who feel they have been discharged from their jobs or discriminated against for having participated in any proceeding under the Act.

H. Employees may serve on the National Advisory Committee on Occupational Safety and Health, in order to advise and consult with the Secretary on all aspects of safety and health programs.

I. Employees must be represented on advisory standard-setting committees.

(1) Each standard promulgated under the Act must assure to the extent feasible that no employee will suffer material impairment of health or functional capacity even if such employee has regular exposure to the hazard dealt with by such standard, for the period of his working life.

(2) Such standards must include requirements for (a) labels or other appropriate forms of warning to alert employees to all hazards to which they are exposed, (b) suitable protective equipment, (c) monitoring of exposure to toxic materials, and (d) medical examinations and tests, including employee access to such records.

J. "Any person adversely affected or aggrieved" by an order of the Commission, can seek "judicial review" by filing a petition with the U. S. Court of Appeals for the circuit in which the employer has his principal office, the circuit in which the violation allegedly occurred, or in the Court of Appeals of the District of Columbia. (This means employee or employee representative.)

K. Should the Secretary of Labor "arbitrarily or capriciously fail to seek relief in an 'imminent danger' situation, any employee who feels he may be injured as a result of such failure, or any authorized employee representative may seek a writ of mandamus in the appropriate U. S. District Court, requiring that the Secretary initiate proceedings for a temporary restraining order and any other relief which can be appropriate."

L. No employee shall be subjected to medical examination, immunization or treatment contrary to his religious beliefs, except where such examination or treatment is necessary to protect the health and safety of others.

M. Employees must have access to any copies of the Act and/or applicable safety and health standards furnished to employers by OSHA. If an employee is denied permission to review the Act or standards during working hours, he must be afforded access to the documents after work on the same day the request is made or at another suitable time.

N. Employees cannot be fined or cited.

O. "Each employee shall comply with the occupational safety and health standards and all rules, regulations, and orders issued pursuant to this Act which are applicable to his own actions and conduct."

20. Employer rights and responsibilities

A. "Each employer shall furnish to each of his employees employment and a place of employment which are free from recognized hazards that are causing or likely to cause death or serious physical harm to his employees, and shall comply with the occupational safety and health standards promulgated under this Act."

B. The employer can enforce the compliance responsibilities of his employees.

(1) He must determine his own enforcement program. Nothing specifies what it should be or how it should be done, except to indicate that the responsibility is his. Such an enforcement program *could* include: (a) a warning letter to employee on first violation; (b) a three-day layoff on second violation; and, (c) discharge on third violation. A careful reading of the Act reveals that the backup for this is the Act itself, not the Compliance Officer, not the Area or Regional Director, nor the Secretary himself. This applies equally to management and labor, employer and employee —and is not a means for jurisdictional argument or contract negotiation, or collective bargaining.

C. The employer shall conduct, proffer or make possible those educational programs necessary for the achievement of some specific requirements under the Act, (see noise abatement and hearing conservation programs heading) and also the goals and objectives of the Act generally.

D. The employer can appeal citations, assessments, penalties, and decisions to OSHRC, U. S. District Court of Appeals, and, if so desired, to the Supreme Court.

E. The employer can apply for and secure valid and justifiable variances.

F. The employer can, on his own and through industry associations, seek and suggest valid and justifiable changes in the standards.

G. The employer can make application to the Small Business Administration for loans to assist him in the purchase of gear, equipment, engineering design, building, etc. related to the achievement of the goals and objectives of the Act and its compliance requirement.

H. The employer can, by attitude, good faith, willingness to improve safety performance, and past history, secure reductions in assessments, fines and penalties.

21. Variances: The Secretary may grant variances, temporary or extended, from occupational health and safety standards (or provisions of standards) in situations where an employer:

A. must increase his staff or enlarge his facilities in order to comply with the standard,

B. can provide working conditions as safe and as healthful as those he would be required to maintain if he complied with the standard,

C. is taking part in a worker safety or health experiment.

When an employer is unable to comply with a standard by its effective date, he may petition the Secretary of Labor for a temporary order granting a variance from the standard. This is only granted after employees have been notified of the employer's request and are afforded an opportunity for a hearing. The Secretary, however, may issue one interim order which will be effective until a decision is made on the basis of a hearing.

The temporary order remains in effect until such time as the employer can come into compliance with the standard, or for one year, whichever is shorter, and may be renewed twice, as long as the employer continues to meet the requirements of the temporary order, *and* if the renewal application is filed at least 90 days before the expiration date of the order. No interim renewal of an order may remain in effect for longer than 180 days.

All temporary orders must prescribe the methods and practices the employer must adopt while the order is in effect, and they must set forth, in detail, his plan for coming into compliance with the standard. To qualify for a temporary variance, -an employer must establish that:

A. he is unable to comply with the standard due to unavailability of qualified personnel, required material or equipment, or because "necessary construction or alteration of facilities cannot be completed by the effective date,"

B. he is taking all possible steps to safeguard his employees against hazards covered by the standard,

C. he has an effective plan for coming into compliance with the standard "as quickly as practicable."

He must submit to the Secretary an application containing the following information:

A. specification of the standard or portion of the standard from which he seeks a variance,

B. a representation, supported by qualified persons, having first-hand knowledge of the facts represented, that he is unable to comply with the standard (or portion thereof) including the reasons for inability to comply,

C. a detailed statement of the measures he has taken and will take to protect employees against the hazard covered by the standard, together with the dates or target dates for such actions,

D. a detailed statement of the measures he has taken or will take to comply with the standard, together with the dates corresponding to such action and the target date for compliance with the standard,

E. certification that he has informed his employees of this application for variance by furnishing a copy of that application to their authorized representative, by posting a summary of that application, by specifying where employees might examine a copy, and by other appropriate means. (The certification should include a description of what the employer has done to inform his employees.)

22. Inspection procedures: Inspections must occur during regular working hours and at other reasonable times, within reasonable limits, in a reasonable manner, and may include private questioning of any employer, owner, operator, agent, or employee. In other words, "during regular working hours and in a manner which does not necessarily disrupt normal business procedures."

The Compliance Officer must, upon entering the workplace:

A. present credentials to the owner, operator, or agent in charge. If, however, within a reasonable time period, an inspector is unable to locate an "agent in charge," he may gain entry by presenting his credentials to any other employee, thus eliminating any time lapse during which an employer could cover up violations of the Act.

B. explain the nature, purpose, and the scope of the inspection, and

C. indicate the records he wants to review and the employees he wants to question.

Advance notice of any inspection not authorized by the Secretary is prohibited and is subject to a fine of not more than $1,000, or imprisonment of not more than six months, or both. Advance notice of the inspection, however, can be given and authorized by the Area Director or Compliance Officer in cases where:

A. such notice will enable an employer to abate dangerous conditions as quickly as possible,

B. the inspection will be conducted after regular business hours, or in circumstances where special preparations are necessary for an inspection.

C. notice is necessary to assure the presence of an employer and employee representative or personnel needed to aid the inspection,

D. other circumstances in which the Area Director or the Compliance Officer, after consultation with the Area Director, determines that notice would permit a more effective inspection.

With rare exception, no notice of inspection may be given more than 24 hours before the scheduled inspection.

An employer representative and an employee representative may accompany the Compliance Officer on his inspection. If there is no duly recognized employee representative, the inspector must consult with a reasonable number of employees regarding conditions of health and safety in the establishment. (He cannot appoint an employee representative as such.)

The right to accompany the Compliance Officer will be denied to anyone who interferes with a fair and orderly investigation. In certain instances the right to accompany the officer may be denied where security matters or trade secrets are involved. In workplaces where groups of employees are represented by different employee representatives, more than one employee representative may accompany the Compliance Officer, or he may be accompanied by different representatives during different phases of the inspection.

Upon completion of inspection, Compliance Officer must confer with the employer or his representative with the employee representative present to advise the employer of safety and health violations which have become apparent as a result of the inspection. The Area Director, after conferral with the inspecting Compliance Officer, sets the proposed amount of the fines, if any.

23. State participation: In keeping with the expressed purpose of assisting and encouraging the states "in their efforts to assume the fullest responsibility," the Act provides options for retention of state jurisdiction in the development of enforcement of health and safety standards. It provides further that even in areas where Federal standards have been established a state may submit its own plan for approval by the Secretary of Labor provided that such plan is at least as effective as the Federal program, and, meets certain specified criteria (see below).

The Act also provides for:

A. procedures permitting interim enforcement of state standards pending final approval of state plans,

B. Federal grants to facilitate the establishment of state programs in furtherance of Congressional safety and health goals, and

C. cooperation between Federal and state agencies in carrying out the objectives of the Act.

A state may have jurisdiction, under state law, over any occupational safety or health issue with respect to which no Federal standard has been promulgated. However, even when Federal occupational health and safety standards have been adopted, any state wishing to assume responsibility for development and enforcement of its own standards may draft and submit for approval by the Secretary of Labor a plan outlining the details of such a program (18h agreement, 18b plan).

The state's plan may deal comprehensively with the problems of health and safety, or may restrict itself to a single hazard or industry. However, any hazards or industries not covered by the state plan will continue to come under Federal jurisdiction.

Eight Requirements for Acceptance of State Plan

(1) Identify the state agency or agencies responsible for administering the plan throughout the state.

(2) Provide for the development and enforcement of health and safety standards which will be at least as effective as Federal standards promulgated under Section 6 of the Act.

(3) Provide for a right of entry and inspection of all workplaces subject to the Act, which is at least as effective as that provided in Section 8, and which includes a prohibition against advance notice of inspections.

(4) Contain assurances that the designated state agency or agencies will have the legal authority and qualified personnel for the necessary enforcement of such standards.

(5) Provide assurances that the state will devote adequate funds to the administration and enforcement of the standards.

(6) Contain assurances that the state, "to the extent permitted by its law," will establish and maintain an occupational safety and health program for all public employees of the state and its political subdivisions, which will be as effective as the program approved in the plan.

(7) Require employers to report to the Secretary in the same manner and to the same extent as if the plan were not in effect.

(8) Provide that the state agency will report to the Secretary in such form as the Secretary shall from time to time require.

Option to Enforce Federal Standards

After approval of the state plan, the Secretary of Labor may, but shall not be required to, exercise his authority to enforce Federal standards. He first determines whether the state plan is operating according to criteria. He does not make this determination until more than three years after state plan is operational.

If the plan is consistent with the criteria, the Secretary of Labor may relinquish his option to enforce Federal standards, and the state will perform those functions related to

(1) employer compliance with standards promulgated under the Act,

(2) inspections, investigations and record keeping,

(3) citations,

(4) procedure for enforcement,

(5) procedures to counteract imminent dangers, and

(6) penalties.

State Plans to be Evaluated

The Secretary is required to evaluate continually the manner in which a state is administering its plan. This evaluation is based on reports submitted by the state agency and information obtained through his own inspections. If the Secretary finds that any state, after due notice and opportunity for a hearing, has failed to comply substantially with any provision of its plan, he must notify the state agency that he is withdrawing approval of the plan.

Upon receipt of such notice by the state agency, the plan will cease to be in effect, and the Secretary may reassert his full authority under the Act.

The State can petition the U. S. Court of Appeals (within 30 days) for review of the Secretary's decision. Judgment of that Court can be subject to review by the U. S. Supreme Court.

Contents of 18h Agreement (State's application)

1. A brief description of each standard which will be covered by the agreement, including pertinent legislative or regulatory citations, a description of the safety and health issue covered by each standard, and a listing of the employments, hazards and establishments which will be covered.

2. The names, addresses and telephone numbers of the state agency or agencies responsible for administering and enforcing the state standard(s), in addition to the names, addresses and tele-

phone numbers of the heads of such agencies. (These requirements do not apply to any agency having only judicial or quasi-judicial responsibilities.)

3. A description of the enforcement program and procedures of each agency administering the standards, containing any specific information which the Secretary deems necessary.

4. The dollars and "approximate man-years" allocated within each responsible agency during the current and previous fiscal periods, including a description of the fiscal period.

5. Notice of the state's intention to submit a plan under Sec. 18b including the state agency's agreement to, (a) submit a notice of intention to file a Sec. 18b plan within 60 days following publication in the Federal Register of procedures for submission and approval of such plans, and (b) submit a plan within the prescribed 60-day period, which may be expected to meet the requirements for state plans with little or no modification thereof.

6. A brief description of the Federal standards dealing with the same issues as the standards which are the subject of the agreement.

7. Provisions under which the Secretary shall inform the state agency of his enforcement activities within the state with respect to the Federal standards referred to in the agreement and provisions requiring the state agency to make such report to the Secretary he may deem necessary with regard to activities performed under terms of the agreement.

8. Any other provisions the Secretary may deem "appropriate" under the circumstances of the standards issue involved.

CHAPTER FOUR
Safety Coordinator/Director

SELECTION

Until the passage of the Act the position of safety director was a neglected one. As a result truly qualified and competent safety personnel are now critically limited in number.

To overcome this, training programs, safety and health curriculi at the university level, enabled by grants from HEW-NIOSH are currently being developed. Numerous organizations conduct and sponsor specialized short courses in safety and health. It is going to take a long time, however, for the newly-trained supply to meet a very critical demand. The Act and its requirements will create literally thousands of new jobs across the country. For example, our forecast for the Region X area, Washington, Oregon, Idaho and Alaska, is 3,500 administrative and support jobs in the five years following 1973. If you multiply that by ten regions this could add up to 30—40,000 new jobs in safety and health.

The Act is said to embrace and cover some 62 million workers. This figure is the total within the federal administration of the Act. If we add to that workers who will be covered in addition in all political subdivision sectors—the federal by presidential decree, state, county and city by state administration of state legislated Acts—we might settle on some 120 million workers in total.

If we approximate the numbers of personnel engaged in the responsibility of safety, present and future, at 50,000, each safety and health administrator and support worker would be responsible for some 2,000 workers. If any qualified and competent safety professional were asked what he thinks can really be accomplished and achieved with 2,000 workers, his answer in all candor would be, "Not much."

There is no question that any company applying itself assiduously and intelligently along the lines suggested herein can *adequately* manage its safety and health problem within its own presently established structure. There is no question, equally, that adequate is not going to be enough.

To practically, economically and profitably achieve the requirements and specifications of the Act, any company of 100 employees or over is going to need to either (1) employ a full time safety director as such, or (2) use professional safety expertise on some kind of consulting basis. For the present, business and industry will have to make do with what it has and what is available.

The safety and health responsibility should be that of one person who is educated and trained for the job as much as is possible. Most of today's qualified safety directors, managers or coordinators, have learned by doing. Great numbers of them have simply been pressed into service when the need arose as the only company employee available at that time, sometimes with and sometimes without qualification. Very few of them have graduated from a college or a university with a major in safety and health as such. Some have college degrees in engineering, industrial hygiene, or nursing—the closest approximation to the specific safety requirement.

The really capable safety professional, the learn-it-the-hard-way, do-it-yourselfer, is already at work for a company which discovered long before the Act came into existence that loss control, accident prevention and safety were an integral part of profitable operation.

In selecting a safety coordinator, it would be best to select a candidate—perhaps from your safety committee—with a demonstrated ability to develop, organize, present and conduct a project or a program, somebody with a recognizable ability to communicate effectively, to get along well with his fellows, to secure their respect, and to handle the leadership role. No one individual will combine all the talents you are seeking, but someone will have capabilities in one or more of these areas. That individual should be the safety coordinator, and should be assigned the OSHA-1970 responsibility.

The newly appointed safety coordinator should be trained with whatever training and education programs are available. Classes in management and communication techniques are essential. Any courses in safety and health, on a continuing or extended education basis, with or without credit, are recommended. A curriculum at any kind of university or college level that is part of either an undergraduate or post graduate degree program would be an extremely desirable part of any educational or training program for any safety personnel.

The safety coordinator should be educated and trained as comprehensively and competently as the rest of the supervisory and management employees. He should also be placed on a report-direct basis to top-level management. Place him at this trainee level in some kind of line of management function and participation where the importance of the job is recognized and not second-rated.

If a safety and health director is hired who is already qualified by experience, background, training and education, the above suggestions still apply, but there are obviously some factors already in your favor. For example, he already knows his job, he is probably thoroughly acquainted with the Act, but this must be verified. He knows the business and the people in it. He usually knows what to do, how to do it, and if not, where to go and who to get to do it. He is usually well versed in the training, education and information roles involved in the safety business. He has probably attended most of the good courses, seminars, conferences and meetings, not only on safety but in management techniques and other disciplines. Another interesting fact about him is that he usually has a rather uniquely broad, across-the-board contact with a large segment of the business, industrial, governmental (national, state and local), medical, legal, insurance, professional safety, and community, life. However, he needs several things he has seldom secured prior to the passage of the Act. He needs to report directly to top management—president, executive vice president, owner. And he needs to be a part of top line management, of equal importance, status and income with that level of management. He needs to be heard on all issues related to safety and health programming and the successful management of it. No annual budgets should be established without considering what expenditures are needed to meet standards requirements of the Act. He should be required to give his opinions on those areas of function, operation and production directly related to his profession, expertise and responsibility.

Perhaps for the first time in your business you are going to need a competent, capable, well trained and educated, experienced, practical and toughminded, human-related and profit-oriented safety and health professional.

THE SAFETY DIRECTOR

The safety director, as capable and experienced as he may be, must realize that safety management has changed. Whether corporate director of safety for the largest company in the United States, director of safety for the biggest labor union, chairman of the federal safety council, or manager of the various safety councils, trade associations, industrial or business organizations around the nation, each person must see that what *has* been done is not enough. There is still a great deal to be accomplished, and safety directors should consider the following as they work.

1. Assess yourself and the problem you face as the leader, guider and director of the problem, challenge and opportunity the Williams-Steiger Occupational Safety and Health Act of 1970, or its state version, presents.

2. Do not be content with the old established ways. Use only those that apply, and develop new approaches, methods and means.

3. Become thoroughly, painstakingly acquainted with the Act. Look carefully at some of its implications, notably employee relations.

4. Make it work *for* you, your company, and your charges. Don't work against it, wasting time in wheelspinning complaint or criticism.

5. Be realistic about your ability. As remarkably well-informed as you may be, don't think you have all the answers.

6. Organize a safety and heath committee. Assess or reassess it in terms of (a) better representation from management, (b) broader representation from total company structure, (c) representation from unions involved, (d) better representation from and contact with, employees, and (e) reorientation of goals and objectives.

7. Develop your own plans, programs, ways and means, costs involved, and annual budget. Submit this to management as a matter of record and recommendation.

8. Maintain and keep a cost-accounting record of your department and all costs related to safety and health programming.

9. See that the OSHA-1970 and state version story is told to all company personnel. Do this by:

A. flip chart presentation and other visuals,

B. posting of notices, memos, records and reports,

C. publication of information relevant to the Act,

D. meetings with employees, and

E. securing guest experts, authorities, and officials to speak or make presentations on the Act.

10. Attend all relevant meetings, conferences, congresses, and seminars on the Act.

11. See that key members of safety and health committees and representatives from management attend as many of these as practicable.

12. Conduct, or cause to be conducted, specialized courses on safety and health, management and communicating techniques, motivation, instruction and training on the Act and any of its specific phases.

13. Take whatever accredited safety and health courses you can.

14. Run a very careful, specific and detailed assessment of the standards applicable to your company. Organize and direct "self-inspections." Determine what needs to be done, and get it done.

15. Determine and list all available information sources relevant to the Act.

16. Subscribe to any informational services you consider useful.

17. Compile a list of OSHA and state personnel, names, addresses, and telephone numbers. Know who they are, what they do, and how they can be of assistance.

18. Get to know these people by other than just name, rank and serial number. They have a job to do, but they are also human beings.

19. Join and participate in professional societies, safety councils, trade, business and industrial associations. Learn about your fellow professionals, their projects, problems, ideas, plans, and programs.

20. Participate in panels and discussions, make speeches and presentations, and write papers and articles on safety and health.

21. Insist on a report-direct line from you to the principal executive officer in your company.

CHAPTER FIVE
Safety and Health Committee

The Safety and Health Committee should consider the following:
1. Secure as a member the top executive officer in your company. If this is not possible, obtain someone as near the top as you are able.
2. Be sure there is a report-direct line to the top executive.
3. Secure as broad a representation from staff (administrative) and line (operations) management and personnel, as you can obtain (Vice presidents, Directors of Finance, Sales and Marketing, Advertising and Public Relations, Purchasing, Plans and Programming, Engineering, Personnel, Industrial Relations—Managers, Superintendents, Supervisors, Foremen, Leadmen and Employees.)
4. Establish goals and objectives, ways and means of achieving them, meeting dates, and target dates where feasible.
5. Publish this list along with other pertinent data for total company personnel distribution and dissemination.
6. The primary goals and objectives should include:
A. planning, developing, organizing and conducting a safety and health program centered on and directed towards OSHA-1970.
B. include in that plan the rest of the safety and health spectrum —off-the-job, traffic, home, recreational—within practical achievable goals.
7. Other goals:
A. assessment of standards, both federal and state. What are they? How do they apply? What is now being done? What needs to be done?

(1) unstaple the Federal Register, tab it and organize it by sections.

(2) assign these sections to safety and health committee members for evaluation and recommendation on necessary steps to be taken.

(3) determine what needs to be done to comply with the Act.

(4) take whatever action, within company policy and safety and health committee responsibility, is necessary.

B. Become thoroughly acquainted with the Act, with its basic specifications and requirements.

C. Develop and help maintain the Safety Log. (This can be a responsibility of the Committee but is probably the responsibility of the Safety and Health Director/Coordinator/Consultant, if you have one.)

D. Develop, define and delineate duties of all members of the Committee.

E. Publish, post and distribute all relevant information and data developed by the Committee.

F. Attend all meetings, conferences, congresses, seminars on OSHA-1970. See that as many members of the Committee attend as practicable and feasible.

G. Conduct self-inspections regularly. Report all findings to the Committee. Make corrections necessary if possible, and/or report corrections necessary to management.

H. Help develop the enforcement measures necessary to aid employees in effectively managing their responsibility of the "shall comply" requirement of the Act.

I. Help enforce those measures by suggestion, example and leadership, and by reporting.

J. Help develop, conduct and secure programs of information dissemination, training and education for the entire company structure, management and employees.

K. Take specialized courses in safety and health education, instruction and training.

L. Join professional health and safety societies.

M. Join and participate in community, industry, association health and safety councils/committees.

N. Participate as a speaker or panel member at safety meetings other than your own.

Note: The Safety and Health Committee is *not* responsible for compliance under the Act. The employer has the principal responsibility in two phases: "Each employer shall furnish to each of his employees, employment, and a place of employment, which are free from recognized hazards that are causing, or likely to cause, death or serious physical harm to his employees," and he "Shall comply with the occupational safety and health standards promulgated under the Act."

The employee has one principal responsibility: he "Shall comply with safety and health standards as they relate to the workplace."

The Safety and Health Committee, however, can and should be a prime force in helping achieve those compliance requirements for both employer and employee.

Even though a company has a safety and health director, it should without exception have a safety and health committee. If this is not the case, the company has:

1. not grasped the full significance of the Act, its meaning, application and implication,

2. made the task of achieving compliance much more difficult, if not impossible,

3. failed to make use of "many hands" available and necessary to get the job done,

4. missed an excellent employee relations potential, and

5. aborted the built-in opportunity to achieve the goals and objectives of an effective safety and health program as practically, economically, and profitably as possible.

No Safety and Health Director can accomplish this task without a functioning Safety and Health Committee.

CHAPTER SIX
Safety Log

If a safety log is already kept, it should be examined within the context suggested here. This is a first step listed in this guideline for the very important reason that it is a recorded keystone for an effective safety and health program. The items listed below are some suggestions for inclusion in the safety log.

1. Letter of intent (see sample on Page 37). This is a simple letter of intent about the Act, signed by your executive officer, prominently posted, and mailed to all employees.

2. Sample letters of results of audiometric testing of employees (see Noise Abatement and Hearing Conservation Program section.)

3. Names, responsibilities and job outlines of safety and health directors/coordinators/consultants.

4. Names, responsibilities, departments represented, of Safety and Health Committee.

5. Published notice of Safety and Health Committee's objectives and goals, methods and means, regular meeting dates and whatever other information is pertinent.

6. This should originate from a formal resolution by the Safety and Health Committee, which spells out the above specific facts.

7. Copies of all record keeping and reporting pertaining to the Act, or any safety and health programming/function/activity.

8. Records of attendance at safety and health meetings of any description, copies of programs, if possible, and copies of any briefs/summaries prepared as a result.

9. Results of any compliance inspection with dates and details. Copies of any memos, letters, dissemination of information of any kind.

10. Results of self-inspection.

11. Record of any action taken:

A. engineering changes

B. improvement or check-out on specific situations

C. variances applied for or secured

D. appeals to Board of Review or others

12. Enforcement measures adopted: what they are, why they were taken, and what the results were.

13. Education and training measures.

A. classes/courses instituted and conducted in-plant

B. classes/courses attended out-plant

14. Institution of noise abatement and hearing conservation program.

A. when started, deadlines

B. details on areas and workers involved

C. audiometric testing summary

D. engineering approach

E. administrative controls

F. employee personal protective devices

15. Purchase of any equipment, gear, devices, mechanism, or programs.

A. cost

B. what purpose

C. what accomplished

D. for whom issued

16. Membership in professional societies, associations.

A. offices held

B. projects participation

C. special recognition and awards

17. Company participation in, sponsorship of, meetings/conferences/congresses/seminars.

18. Company participation in industry-wide, association, society, safety and health projects, research, scholarships.

19. Published articles or papers by company personnel.

20. Speeches, participation on panels, assistance in organization and conduct of safety and health meetings/congresses/conferences/seminars.

21. Inclusion of all letters, memos, notices of action taken, action recommended, notification, and notices.

LETTER OF INTENT

Dear fellow employee:

The Williams-Steiger Occupational Safety and Health Act of 1970 is now in effect and has been since August 27, 1971. It applies directly to all of us—to us as an employer and to you as an employee. The Act is a "voluntary compliance" law, seeking cooperation from management and labor, employer and employee. Our compliance with the Act specifies that we "shall" provide a safe and healthful work place for every employee. This is accomplished by meeting a set of safety and health standards specified in the Act. Your compliance with the Act requires that you "shall" meet those standards by individually employing safe and healthful work habits. This is also specified in the Act.

Our position and intent on this new and comprehensive Act is to cooperate to the fullest of our ability and to meet its voluntary compliance specifications as successfully and capably as we can possibly manage. You will be hearing more about this in detail as our program for voluntary compliance is devised and implemented. I know I can count on your support, cooperation and assistance in helping our company achieve the much-to-be desired goals and objectives of the Williams-Steiger Occupational Safety and Health Act of 1970.

Thank you for listening.

CHAPTER SEVEN

Noise Abatement and

Hearing Conservation Program

OCCUPATIONAL NOISE STANDARDS
(Reference: Bulletin 334, U. S. Department of Labor)

These standards basically require that a noise abatement and hearing conservation program be instituted by an employer in any workplace where noise levels exceed 90dBA (90 decibels on the "A" scale). The program specifies that:

1. engineering design/controls/measures be taken by the employer to achieve sound levels throughout the work place that do not exceed 90dBA.

2. administrative means be employed in the placement of employees in work areas, which in combination of several exposures above and below 90dBA, add up to a specified number of working hours, or portions thereof, within exposure times and levels, averaging out to 90dBA for an eight-hour working day.

3. personal protective devices (ear plugs, muffs) be made available, used and required for all employees working or entering, either steadily or infrequently, those areas exceeding 90dBA.

4. all employees who either steadily or infrequently work or enter areas exceeding 90dBA be given regular audiometric tests to determine threshold hearing, and that those records be available for inspection by any compliance officer representing either OSHA, or the state agency administering the Act.

5. periodic noise surveys be made in those areas where levels exceed 90dBA to determine what they are in the first place and to check the results of any engineering changes or any change in the noise level.

6. the objective, and end result, as specified in the standards, is that any noise level exceeding 90dBA must be engineered out within some kind of specified time period, insofar as this is feasible. "Feasible" as defined by the guideline is "capable of being done, accomplished or carried out; capable of being dealt with successfully."

7. Noise Surveys

A. A noise survey of each area in the plant in which sound levels exceed 90dBA shall be made at least once a year to ensure that sound levels have not increased above those originally existing.

B. The survey may also establish that noise levels in some area have been reduced to levels below 90dBA and thereby justify discontinuing application of requirement for administrative controls, ear protection, and audiometric tests of individuals in such areas.

C. Noise survey of an area is recommended whenever a change is made in either equipment or type of operations so that significant changes in noise level will be acted upon immediately.

D. Tests of noise levels will be made with a sound level meter on the A-scale, slow response.

E. The sound level meter used will meet ANSI standards.

F. Record of noise survey will show: instrument used, date, time and location of such tests, machinery or equipment generating the noise, name of person making the test.

G. Test records of such surveys will be kept readily available for inspection for one year or until a subsequent survey is made, if done more frequently.

H. The noise survey will be done by an insurance carrier, consultant, representative of a state labor or health department, or by a qualified individual designated by the company.

The following measures, though required and essential, are in a sense substitutes.

1. Administrative Controls

If noise cannot be reduced to permissible intensities by engineering controls, administrative controls should be developed in order to limit duration of workers' exposure to noise levels above 90dBA to the limits explained in Bulletin 334. Some examples:

A. Arrange work schedules so that employees working the major portion of a day at or very near to the 90dBA limits are not exposed to higher noise levels.

B. Ensure that employees who have reached the upper limit of duration for a high noise level work the remainder of the day in an environment with a noise level well below 90dBA.

C. Where the man-hours required for a job exceed the permissible time for one man in one day for the existing sound level, divide the time/work among two, three or as many men as needed, either successively or together, to keep individual noise exposure within permissible time limits.

D. If less than full-time production of a noisy machine is needed, arrange to run it a portion of each day, rather than all day for part of the week.

E. Perform occasional high level noise producing operations at night or at other times when a minimum number of employees will be exposed.

2. Personal Protective Equipment

"If such control fails to reduce sound levels within the levels of the specification, personal protective equipment shall be provided and used to reduce sound levels within the levels permissible."

A. This is considered an interim measure. There are few cases where the use of such equipment is acceptable as a permanent solution.

B. Regulations require both the *provision* and *use* of personal protective equipment. How this is accomplished is up to the employer.

(1) Educational and promotional programs are to precede the initiation of required use of such equipment, and "continue until 100% acceptance by employees."

(2) The absence of an observable high proportion of use constitutes a "violation of the regulation."

AUDIOMETRY

Audiometric tests are to be made of all individuals working steadily or infrequently in areas in which the noise level is 90dBA or above. Audiometric tests may be made as frequently as prescribed by the plant regular or consulting physician, but only under very special conditions should they be made less than once a year. They can be made in a doctor's office or elsewhere outside the plant, providing test facilities, techniques and records are equal to, or exceed, the minimum requirements described below:

A. Test booth or room must meet current ANSI standards.

B. Tests shall consist of an air conduction octave band analysis, ANSI standards, 500, 1,000, 2,000, 3,000 and 4,000, minimally.

C. Audiometric tests must be conducted by persons trained and skilled in audiometric testing.

D. Audiometers must meet the specifications for limited range, pure tone audiometers (ANSI standards).
E. Audiometers must have a certificate of calibration, issued by someone qualified to so certify, before being placed in use.
F. Audiometers shall be calibrated each year thereafter.
G. The current certificate attesting to such calibration shall be ready for inspection.
H. Audiometers shall be subjected to a biological check, preferably once a week but at least once a month, or before each use of the instrument if it is used less than once a month. A log of these checks shall be maintained and be available for inspection.

RECORDS
A. A record of each audiogram made on each individual shall be available for inspection.
B. Records of audiometric tests shall indicate which standard they are based on.
C. Complete records on each employee required to be tested shall be retained for one year following termination of employment or transfer to an area in which noise levels above 90dBA do not exist.
D. Records will be examined for evidence of any deterioration of hearing acuity and of action taken to prevent further deterioration in those employees found to suffer some loss of acuity.
E. Conclusions as to effectiveness of control measures taken will be based on examination of a significant number of audiograms and not upon the basis of one or two cases.

SELECTION OF PERSONAL PROTECTIVE EQUIPMENT
Cotton stuffed in the ears is not acceptable, but fine glass wool is. Wax-impregnated cotton, properly inserted in the ear, if fresh daily and properly used is acceptable. Properly fitted ear-plugs, fitted to the individual, issued by a trained person under the direction of a physician or the physician himself, and frequently checked are acceptable.

Also acceptable are ear muffs. These can be issued by any designated person in the plant. Long hair and spectacle or goggle temples reduce attenuation. The ear protector used must achieve the reduction of the noise level to the permissible specification.

HEARING CONSERVATION PROGRAM
"In all cases where the sound levels exceed the values specified, a continuing, effective hearing conservation program shall be administered." "Continuing" means that the program will be in ef-

fect and in use as long as noise levels above 90dBA occur in the plant. "Effective" means that exposed employees will not suffer continuing deterioration of hearing acuity because of their exposure, but that incipient loss of hearing will be detected and necessary steps taken to prevent any further deterioration before serious hearing loss has occurred.

A. Where the sound level in a working area has not been reduced to 90dBA or below by engineering means, and reliance must be placed on administrative controls to limit duration of exposure, or on ear protection to reduce the sound level actually reaching the ear, a hearing conservation program is required. This is to be applied to all employees whose work brings them either steadily or infrequently into areas where sound levels exceed 90dBA.

COMPLIANCE PLAN

Whenever a noise survey shows noise levels in excess of those listed below, steps necessary to reduce the noise exposure to or below those levels shall be ascertained and a detailed plan, with completion dates for individual steps, shall be prepared. Following the original survey which shows existence of overexposures, the steps in a typical compliance plan might include the following:

1. A detailed survey of sound levels and sound spectra to determine the sources of excessive sound levels.

2. Initiation of engineering studies to determine methods for reducing sound levels at their sources.

3. Planning and initiation of feasible administrative controls, such as modifying production schedules to divide noisy jobs among enough people to bring each below the permissible limit or spreading part-time noisy operations.

4. Initial audiograms for personnel excessively exposed.

5. Installation of a personal protective equipment program.

6. Follow-up audiograms at appropriate intervals to assess effectiveness of the personal protective equipment program and administrative controls.

7. Installation of engineering controls, or process changes to reduce noises at their source.

8. Repeated noise surveys to measure the effectiveness of the engineering changes.

When the compliance plan involves long term enginering projects, it may be revised from time to time as conditions change. The orderly completion on schedule of the various phases of the compliance plan, together with other components of the hearing conservation program, will be considered compliance with the regulation.

COMMENTS ON HEARING CONSERVATION

At the time of the writing of this handbook, OSHA had decided that audiometric testing of employees exposed either steadily or infrequently to noise levels above 90dBA was not mandatory. The reason behind the decision was that the standards, as such, did not contain that exact specification in their terminology.

On the other hand, the Walsh-Healey Public Contracts Act, adopted by Secretarial decision as part of OSHA-1970, specified very plainly, simply and clearly the entire approach on hearing conservation, including mandatory audiometric testing. Very plainly, also, as any OSHA or state staff member, from top official to compliance officer knows, there can be no "effective" hearing conservation program without initial and regular follow-up audiometric testing of employees so exposed.

The hearing conservation standard, as published on page 10518, section 1910.95 of the Federal Register, May 29, 1971, Occupational Noise Standard, paragraph b3 specifies: "In all cases where the sound levels exceed the values shown herein (see below) a continuing *effective* hearing conservation program shall be administered." That *is* mandatory and *in* the standards.

Table G-16, Permissible Noise Exposures

Duration per day hours	Sound level dBA slow response
8	90
6	92
4	95
3	97
2	100
1.5	102
1	105
0.5	110
0.25 or less	115

The Act also states that "exposure to impact noise should not exceed 140 dB peak sound pressure level." This sets the upper limit of sound level to which a person should be exposed, regardless of the brevity of the exposure.

In contrast with the 115dBA upper limit for steady noise, the higher intensity for impact noise is permissible because the noise impulse resulting from impacts, like hammer blows or explosive processes, is past the ear before it has time to react fully. Impact noise levels are to be measured only with an impact meter or oscilloscope.

The key word in this critical part of the hearing conservation program approach is "effective." "Effective" as defined in the U. S. Department of Labor's Bulletin 334 "Occupational Noise Standards Guidelines," means that "exposed employees will not suffer continuing deterioration of hearing acuity because of their exposure, but that incipient loss of hearing will be detected, and necessary steps taken to prevent further deterioration before serious hearing loss has occurred." This is impossible without initial and regular audiometric testing.

It is unfortunate that the issue has to be begged at all, but what about the specific terminology of the Act itself, as adopted by Congress, and signed by the President? "By providing medical criteria which will insure, insofar as practicable, that no employee will suffer diminished health, functional capacity or life expectancy as a result of his work exposure." Whether mandatory audiometric testing finds its way into the specific terminology remains to be seen, and in some ways really makes no difference.

Two interesting possibilities, already inherent and implied, occur with the terminology of the standards, as they are without mandatory audiometric testing as part of the specific wording. Suppose, for instance, that an employee or employee representative requests an inspection on the basis that a hearing conservation program is ineffective without audiometric testing? Or suppose he questions the Secretary's decision as being "harmful" or "capricious"?

Aside from any law, Federal or state, there is another very practical basis and consideration on audiometric testing. The following example illustrates this.

In 1956 the pulp and paper industry in the Pacific Northwest initiated a program to conduct audiometric tests of all employees in an admittedly noisy business. At the outset it was difficult to convince management of the desirability of this because of the fear of possible repercussions from employees if they were informed of the results.

The program's basis was very practical. Compensation was available for partial or total hearing loss or impairment. The need for determining the employer's responsibilty was essential. In this way the hearing loss or impairment for which an employer was responsible could be determined. If he had conducted an initial pre-hire test which identified the degree of hearing loss at that point and no further hearing loss occurred thereafter because of a hearing conservation program that enforced the wearing of individual hearing protection devices, the employer would not be responsible for any of the loss.

The need for a base test was obvious, for otherwise how could an employer institute and enforce the use of personal protective hearing devices without proof that they were needed? How could he keep an employee from suffering further deterioration in hearing ability unless he could establish a base level and then enforce the use of protective hearing devices?

Surprisingly, employee reaction to the program was positive rather than negative, as had been rather apprehensively anticipated. Employees were appreciative. They rather expected, in a high level noise area and job, to suffer some hearing loss and were not recriminatory. They were more amenable to the use of protective hearing devices, and there were very few suits.

The wood products industry, though certainly not universally so, followed the lead of one of its component members, and for some years, prior to passage of any federal or state legislation, used audiometric tests for employees regularly in high level noise areas.

The state of Oregon, in its 1972 legislation, adopted a measure requiring initial and annual audiometric testing of all employees exposed to noise levels 90dBA and above. It also passed stringent requirements relating to time off the job prior to testing: 12 hours for 90-94.99dBA, 14 hours for 95-99.99dBA, and 16 hours for 100-plus dBA.

Other states will probably duplicate Oregon's legislation to some degree. This undoubtedly emanates directly and originally from the Williams-Steiger Occupational Safety and Health Act of 1970 and its clearly indicated Congressional intent, even though the Occupational Safety and Health Administration was cautiously ambivalent when this was written.

There are many reasons, then, for initiating a hearing conservation program as guidelined in Bulletin 334. The first is most important for the employer genuinely concerned about his workers.
1. Job-related, noise-induced hearing loss or impairment is, almost without exception, irreversible and permanent.
2. The probability is that both federal and state laws and standards will make audiometric testing mandatory.

3. States that presently have workmen's compensation laws make compensability awards on partial or total hearing loss.

4. Employers need to know what part of the hearing loss, if any, can be charged to them, a vital reason for an initial base level hearing acuity test.

5. Employers need to know if the employee's hearing loss or impairment stays static, with the enforced use of protective hearing devices, or deteriorates. Follow-up regular audiometric testing will reveal this.

6. Employers need to be able to post employees on hearing loss or impairment problems so that the employee can take whatever medical action is necessary, advisable or desired.

7. Employees need a good reason for wearing protective hearing devices.

8. Either employers or unions can initiate audiometric testing as part of a hearing conservation program.

9. As touchy as it is, and as infrequently as it has been employed to date, the possibility of suit cannot be overlooked.

Once the testing has been instituted, employees should be notified of the results of the individual audiometric test. It is not necessary or required that the employee see the test card or audiometric readout. As a matter of fact, interpreting it can be done only by either a qualified, professional audiologist or a physician. But the employee should have the results interpreted for him.

As a matter of further and very important fact, while the audiometric testing can be done by qualified technicians, and while the read-out *can* be done by an audiologist, the Act specifies that it shall be done under the direction of a physician. Also, to be medically and legally acceptable, all audiometric readouts must be signed by a physician, not an audiologist.

Several form letters of notification, which were employed and used successfully for several years by the Weyerhaueser Company in its hearing conservation program, are included here. These can be adapted to meet your needs whether you are conducting your hearing conservation program in-company or having it done by some outside agency.

LETTER TO EMPLOYEE REPORTING
HEARING TEST RESULTS

Company:	Summit Timber Company
Location:	Darrington Washington
Date:	January 13, 1972
From:	(Company Official)
Subject:	Periodic Hearing Tests
To:	George A. Armstrong (Individual Tested)

Your initial hearing test on, January 12, shows that:

(date)

(X) Your hearing is essentially normal in all the tones tested.
( ) You show evidence of loss in the higher tones.
( ) You show evidence of loss in the lower tones.
( ) You show evidence of loss in both the higher and lower tones.
While the Occupational Safety and Health Act of 1970 requires that you wear acceptable protective hearing devices continuously on the job, we recommend it even more basically to you as a necessary an practical health measure, to, (1) prevent hearing loss, or, (2 prevent any further hearing loss.
Thank you.
Physician,
  Charles M. McGill,
  M.D., M.P.H.

ANNUAL AUDIOGRAM FORM LETTER

Company
Location
Date
From
Subject
To
Your periodic hearing test on, _____, shows that there has been no change in your hearing since your last test on, _____.
Your hearing is essentially normal in all the tones tested.
It is recommended that you continue to wear ear plugs or muffs on the job continuously, to preserve your normal hearing.

  Signature
  Physician,
  Company Official

ANNUAL AUDIOGRAM FORM LETTER
Company
Location
Date
From
Subject
To
Your periodic hearing test on, ＿＿＿＿＿＿, shows that there has been no change in your last test on, ＿＿＿＿＿＿. However, there is some evidence of some prior loss in the higher tones which still persists.

It is recommended that you continue to wear ear plugs or muffs on the job continuously to prevent further hearing loss. Continued protection will prevent your high tone loss from progressing to the lower tones, which are the important ones for the understanding of the human voice in conversation.

If there are any questions about these results and/or recommendations, please check with (Company department) for clarification.

   Signature
   Physician,
   Company Official

ANNUAL AUDIOGRAM FORM LETTER
Company
Location
Date
From
Subject
To
Your periodic hearing test on, ＿＿＿＿＿＿, shows that there has been no change in your hearing since your last test on, ＿＿＿＿＿＿
However, there is some evidence of some prior loss in both the higher and lower tones which still persists.

It is recommended that you continue to wear ear plugs or muffs on the job continuously to prevent further hearing loss. Hearing in the lower tones must be preserved to adequately understand the human voice in conversation.

If there are any questions about these results and/or recommendations, please check with (Company department) for clarification.

   Signature
   Physician,
   Company Official

ANNUAL AUDIOGRAM FORM LETTER
Company
Location
Date
From
Subject
To

Your periodic hearing test on, _____, shows a significant change since your last test on, _____. Since then you have lost some hearing in, _____; _____; _____.

           Low tones   high tones   low and high tones

It is recommended that you:

( ) Wear ear plugs or muffs continuously on the job to prevent further hearing loss.

( ) Return for a hearing check in _____ months instead of the usual interval. Call the (Company department) before coming in for the test.

( ) Come in to the (Company department) to talk to a doctor about your test.

If there are any questions about these results and/or recommendations, please check with the (Company department) for clarification.

Signature
Physician,
Company Official

CHAPTER EIGHT

Communication and Education

INFORMATION DISSEMINATION

This Act applies to practically every workplace, and everyone in that workplace. Be sure, therefore, that everyone knows what the Act is, what it is all about, how it applies.

This is neither simple nor easy. It is, however, necessary and advisable.

1. Begin with management and supervisory personnel.

A. If at all possible, turn your top executive officer out for at least one informational conference on the Act.

He is going to have a difficult time believing it to begin with— no matter how capably *you* tell it. It helps to hear it in person, first-hand.

B. Get other management personnel out to informational conferences and meetings on the Act. Safety Councils, business and industrial associations, professional organizations, sponsor such meetings. OSHA conducts them. State offices hold them. Go and find out.

C. Arrange a meeting of your own management and supervisory group—preferably with some representative of either the federal or state Act as part of it.

Note: If a compliance officer is part of it, hold the meeting away from your plant or place of business. By terms of his job specification a compliance officer must make an inspection any time he visits your plant.

Call your state department of labor or corresponding agency. Check with OSHA, area or region headquarters. Check with your local safety council or chapter of the American Society of Safety Engineers.

2. Going to meetings does not always accomplish the objective you may be seeking. We know of some who, after several conferences didn't really grasp the full significance of the Act, some who still don't, and some who never will.

Management—in any form—sometime‾ does not really believe the Act, its state parallel, that it is here, that it means what it says, that it applies to your business—until a compliance officer shows up to inspect the facility.

Inspection, as such, is certainly one way to learn about it—but it can be costly, irritating, frustrating and really, inexcusable.

So get the "boss" out, for at least one meeting where he hears the word first hand.

Let's re-emphasize the need for somebody to be fully acquainted with the Act, to be charged with its responsibility, and see that management is as fully acquainted with it, by memo, by report, by summary, however it is formally managed—on paper.

3. Begin to get the word out to employees. The Act says, "The employer shall notify the employee of his rights and obligations, and with reasonable particularity of the standards that are applicable, by notice and by other means."

There is a printed poster, "SAFETY AND HEALTH PROTECTION ON THE JOB", the centerpiece in your Record Keeping Requirements brochure, which must be displayed in a prominent place in the establishment to which your employees normally report to work.

That is only a beginning. Don't leave it at that.

4. Conduct, or cause to be conducted, informational meetings on the Act, standards, specifications, requirements, rights and responsibilities, for employees. For *all* employees.

5. Employees are going to need to know about the Act—just as you do, in order to:

A. Help the company in the achievement of its compliance program.

B. Understand their rights *and* responsibilities under the Act and its standards.

C. Understand the company's rights and responsibilities, and problems, in achieving compliance.

D. Know the need and necessity to comply individually in the development of, and adherence to, safe and healthful work habits.

6. Employers, unions or other outside agencies, can accomplish the employee dissemination discussed here. The employer's decision is a very simple one. How important is it for who to do it?

TRAINING AND EDUCATION

In support of your program of information dissemination, you will need to conduct, cause to be conducted, or send personnel to:

1. Specialized courses in general safety and health subjects.

2. Specialized courses with specific relationship to the Act, standards, or portions thereof.

3. Regular meetings on aspects of, and instruction in, the Act, such as:

A. noise abatement and hearing conservation program.

B. use of personal protective equipment devices.

C. first aid.

4. Specialized courses in leadership, management techniques, motivation and communicating techniques, public relations and information.

5. Meetings, conferences, seminars, congresses on safety and health, for a broader exposure to the problem as such, and to get acquainted with the ways, means, methods employed by others in their approach to the problem.

6. Enrollment in those courses at the vocational school, junior college or university level, with or without credit, that will help your personnel achieve a more effective safety and health program.

PUBLIC RELATIONS—INFORMATION

You would do well to use your safety and health program as a valid means of positive, meaningful and valuable contact with your community.

1. Make any noteworthy event or function, related to the Act, the subject of regular news coverage for your house organ, newsletter, or simple memo to all personnel.

2. Employ the same tactic with your local newspaper(s), radio and TV station(s).

3. Seek opportunities to speak, make presentations—at service clubs, chambers of commerce, professional societies, trade and industrial associations, PTA's, and other community meeting places and forums.

4. See that those in your company with real expertise on the Act are participants as panel members, principal speakers, at safety and health conferences—and notify your local news media of that participation.

5. Use your safety and health program—or an interesting aspect of it—for an advertisement, or a series of ads.

Remember that what makes news is that it is:

(1) Newsworthy.

(2) Interesting.

(3) Different.

(4) Unusual.

(5) Unique.

Remember that what makes the wastebasket is that it is:

1. Too commercial—like an advertisement for the company.

You don't have to be an accomplished writer or reporter to get a story in the news media. They will *re-write whatever* you turn in anyhow. Just:

1. Compile the facts on a who, what, when, where, why and how basis.

2. Typewrite the facts on a clean sheet of 8½ x 11 paper.

3. Double space the lines.

4. Do an original (no carbons, Xeroxes or duplicates, please).

5. Put the date, your name and telephone number where you can be reached, at the top of the release.

6. Fold the release in half—typed copy out.

7. Mail it, or take it into the city desk, the news editor of a radio or TV station.

8. Sometimes you can solve the entire problem by calling the city desk, or the news editor, who may assign you a reporter to do, or take, the story over the phone.

9. Be sure all names are complete, accurate and spelled right.

Put safety and health stories actively to work in your house organ, if you have one. With pictures.

Include such things as:

(1) Broad corporate policy decisions on major decisions related to the Act.

(2) Initiation of special programming. Hearing conservation, for example. Special training of personnel. Enrollment in safety and health classes by company personnel.

(3) Engineering changes or installation of new equipment to cope with standards requirements of the Act.

(4) Awards or incentive programs for personnel.

Write and send articles to business, industrial and trade associations.

Send notices of any speeches, presentations made by company personnel, to professional society and trade association publications.

Solicit opportunities for acknowledged specialists in your company to appear on panels, programs, presentations.

MOTIVATIONAL AND COMMUNICATING TECHNIQUES
(How to Get the Job Done)

The Act provides the essential, basic and necessary legal framework for getting the job done, but doing it is still up to us, an individual elective employer and employee.

Achieving the real objectives of the Act—the saving of lives, the reduction in numbers, severity and cost of job-related injuries and illnesses—is almost totally dependent upon, "saying it so they hear it."

That's why the information dissemination, training and education, and public relations and information processes mentioned previously are so important.

Here are some cardinal guidelines for communication, one to one, one to several and several to several, to put to work.

1. The basic purposes of all communication is—to learn who we are, what we are, what we sound like, what we need to do to survive.

2. The secondary purpose of all communication is—to move others to some kind of action. (Belief, acceptance of an idea, doing something about it).

Consider the following precepts, as bald and as unqualified as some may sound.

1. Man's principal function on earth is—survival. Learning what to do, what not to do, how to do it,—to survive.

2. Man is not born equal. He is unequal in many, many ways. His "equalness," if you prefer to interpret it that way, is in his very "unequalness." His differences, one from another. His unique-

ness. His sole and exclusive ownership of a set of fingerprints un-
duplicated anyplace else in the world, or in time.
3. Man is *not* seeking "equality" as such. He does *not* want to be
the "equal" of somebody else. He is rather seeking the real in-
alienable right of mankind—the right to be his own man, the
miraculously *different* and *unique* individual he was created to be.
He is seeking the right to fulfill that individuality to the best of
his ability—and the acknowledgement by others of that simple
truth, image and personality, within those limitations set by society
for its group as well as its individual survival.
4. Man looks for *acknowledgement* from his peers and others of
his *membership in the human race*. He wants no handicaps in *that*
equality, but he does not want to be the equal of somebody. He
wants to excel by means of his own personal, individual, and in
a sense, "unequal" talents.
5. Man, therefore, wants to, deserves to, be treated in that context of equality as a *fellow human being,* but *individually* as a
person.
6. He also, therefore, will not be, does not want to be: looked
down on, tolerated or put up with; treated as an inferior; put upon
or dealt with unfairly or dishonestly; the object of unwarranted
disapproval or criticism; considered stupid, unintelligent, incapa-
ble, inadequate; set apart, segmented, classified, alienated, or
even, in many instances, integrated.
7. He is basically motivated by "self interest"—*however* you happen to define that—practically, philosophically, psychologically, so-
ciologically and physiologically.

If it does something for him, he will listen to it. *He may,* in
fact, even *hear you the way you thought you said it—and do it.*

Man, regardless of how sophisticated or knowledgeable, intellec-
tual or learned, how far he has progressed up the ladder of suc-
cess, however you may define him, is a survivor, whose every talent and capability is directed toward that objective.

Starting from that stringent, but nonetheless realistic, objective
and practical ground zero from the standpoint of *your* survival as
a would-be effective communicator, keep the following dynamics
in mind.
1. All really good communicators are apprehensive, nervous, or
just plain scared. That includes the biggest and the best of them,
the most successful pros in the business.

Plainly and simply, if you are not, you are certain to bomb out
with your audience.

That trembling, shaky, uncomfortable unease, is a physiological reaction to a psychological stimulus—adrenalin pumping into your blood stream to help you meet a crisis or emergency.

No crisis for you? No reaction from your body? No response from your audience? *Dullsville!*

2. All really good communicators know their subject forward and backward.

3. All really good communicators organize their information and material with great care and attention to detail.

4. All really good communicators rehearse assiduously and at length. Call it anything else you like—but rehearsal is its name.

5. All really good communicators establish an immediate rapport with their audience—by taking into account some of the precepts we have discussed above; by talking *to* their audience, not down to or at them; by including all of their audience, looking directly at them—in the eye, responding and reacting to them; by working diligently to secure just that objective—to be one with your audience.

6. All really good communicators take some pains ahead of time to find out about the audience, who they are, what they are, likes, dislikes, prejudices, hangups, no-no's.

7. All really good communicators have a "game plan." Some speak completely—or seemingly—ad lib, some speak from notes, some memorize, some read. Memorizing and/or reading is not necessarily recommended, but whatever works best for you, do it, and be sure you have some kind of formalized plan of action, continuity or performance.

8. All really good communicators adapt to the situation—remain flexible even within a formalized "plan of action" to be able to adjust to the situation as it develops, or as it may change for some reason or other.

9. All really good communicators manage such things as "inflection," "gestures," "presentation" by:

A. Observing all the precepts we have mentioned

B. Knowing the subject thoroughly and being thoroughly prepared

C. Enthusiasm

Such dynamics as "inflection," "gestures," "presentation," spring naturally, becomingly and emphatically out of the three bases we have noted above.

If they are "practiced," "contrived," or used consciously, they are apt to detract from the presentation.

10. All really good communicators, insofar as is practical and possible, "case the joint" ahead of time. Take the time to take an in-person look at the place of presentation and any problems pre-

sented thereto. Particularly if you are using audio visual aids.

11. All really good communicators develop, employ, and use any audio-visual aid helpful to the cause. Make sure ahead of time they are set up, functioning and ready to go.

12. All really good communicators (even though they may suffer the torture of the damned) love, enjoy and have fun communicating. If *you* don't—forget it.

NOTE

Everything mentioned above applies in some degree to every communicating situation in which you find yourself. Conversation with somebody, command decisioning as a foreman, supervisor, superintendent, manager, director, vice-president, president, or chairman of the board.

Making presentations, speeches, awards, acceptances. Acting, singing, entertaining, performing. *To name a few.*

Perhaps the most difficult of all—all really good communicators are excellent listeners.

EMPLOYEE RELATIONS

Many authorities on the Act and its implications consider it as much an employee relations bill as a safety and health dictum. Its employee relations aspect, effectively implemented, is noteworthy, considerable, and has a practical potential which is almost entirely overlooked.

To begin with, no legislation as such accomplishes a specified objective of itself. It needs people, people working together, cooperating, contributing, participating, seeking a mutually profitable, desirable and achievable goal.

Look at the *real* goals of the Act—although not specified there in the terminology below.

1. Saving life.

2. Reducing the numbers, severity and cost of job related accidents and illnesses.

3. Helping establish the security and well-being of those who work with and for us, who help get the job done.

4. Profit-making.

Profit-making?

That's right. Business and industry, with minimal exception, have never tied the cost of accidents to profit-making—or profit-losing.

Production, production increase, more efficient production, uninterrupted production, has been the traditional answer—not preventive protectivity.

If a preventable accident occurs involving, for example, $100,000 in direct costs, to an employee, however that spells out or adds up —it has to be $100,000 in lost profit.

If insurance rates for a company are increased because of an accelerating accident frequency ratio, that could be reduced or at least held static by effective loss control, accident prevention, safety and health programming measures—the increase in rate has to add up to lost profit.

Traditionally, safety has gone begging. Perhaps this is due to the fact that production modes, changes, are specific, tangible, observable and assessable. Accident prevention, loss control, safety management, is seemingly intangible, hard to fix and assess in numbers and results, and requiring in many ways faith in things unseen, demonstrating little in terms of cold, logical and recognizable return.

If we come back to those four goals again, we will look for a long time before we find anything more in the favor of both the employer and employee as a practical meeting ground for partnering-up accomplishments, or anything more in their mutual self interest.

Many employer or management people are apprehensive, if indeed not downright bitter about the "employee rights" aspect of the Act. Justifiable or not, one thing for certain is—that it is not realistic.

It also overlooks a vitally important plus that employees rights within the Act specification represents. It is only a negative if viewed that way by management—and if that is the overt or covert attitude of management, it not only can be, but is a real negative.

If, for example, management positions itself against the Act, demonstrates its opposition to it in whatever observable form, it is not only readily evident *to* employees, but carries along with it an also obvious message.

1. Sorry. Your life and limb and health don't really mean that much to us.

2. We're really not interested in you.

3. After money you come first.

There are all kinds of legitimate, valid reasons for disagreeing with the mechanics and the niggling detail of the Act—but obvious and expressed disagreement with its basic principles is like arguing against mother love.

Viewed positively and practically, as an excellent employee relations opportunity, what are some of the steps that could be taken?
1. We have already suggested a number of them in the preceding pages.
2. Develop a position paper that clearly defines company philosophy, attitude, policy and programming approach.
3. Be sure that all management and supervisory personnel is thoroughly acquainted with that position and adheres to it. (No gripers or cry-babies please, particularly in leadership positions.)
4. Let your employees—all employees—know what that position is.
5. State the problem the Act and compliance with it poses the company, employer *and* employee.
6. Secure involvement and participation in solutions to the problem from as broad a representative group, from total company structure, as you can possibly manage.
7. Solicit answers to the problem from total company personnel.
8. Act on these solutions and answers immediately, or as soon as possible. If action must be delayed, be sure the reasons for it are specified, explained and understood.
9. Institute some kind of awards program.
10. Actively foster, support and participate in:
A. Information dissemination to total company structure.
B. Education and training programs.
C. Membership in professional safety and health societies, organizations, councils, committees.
D. Meetings, conferences, seminars, congresses on safety and health.
11. Trust and include employees as equal, responsible, interested, contributing, participating and vitally important members of the company production team.

Since the first employer rewarded or paid the first employee for the work performed, a relationship was forged as unbreakable as the simple need to survive for both. Different in degree, but nonetheless the same basically, and made possible *by* that employment.

That simple relationship, a kind of silver cord, employer to employee does exist. Employees, generally speaking, are loyal to their employer. Their first allegiance on the job is to that employer. There is therefore a working relationship—employer to employee—that can be interrupted, bargained and bartered, but not severed as long as the worker works for the man who hired him and who pays his wages.

Employers have a lot more going for them in this relationship than they are inclined to think.

Employee rights, as specified in the Act, have faced the employer, perhaps for the first time, with some specific decisions he has not had to make prior to the passage of the Act.

Since real compliance with the Act, the achievement of its goals and objectives, in its end result is totally dependent upon people, how they think, respond, react, cooperate and participate, it behooves the employer from a practical standpoint alone to take every means possible to make employee rights work *for* him.

Employees are quick to learn the company attitude, and equally quick to respond in duplicate.

The Act, believe it or not, is a remarkable employee relations opportunity for the employer, and member-relations opportunity for the unions.

As a perhaps noteworthy comment on this aspect of the Williams-Steiger Occupational Safety and Health Act of 1970, listen.

At an annual industrial safety conference I stepped out of a session in which a management representative made a rather large point, in front of an equally large audience, of the fact that management had vigorously opposed the Act, from its outset.

Standing in a small conversational group in the corridors of this meeting area we were joined by, and introduced to, a man who turned out to be a rather high ranking labor official. He was irked by what he had just heard in that same session, as indeed was I.

After some pros and cons on the subject, the following statement was made:

"If we're not careful," he said, "the worker is going to make an end run around both of us—management *and* labor."

CHAPTER NINE

Index to Part 1910

OCCUPATIONAL SAFETY AND HEALTH STANDARDS
FEDERAL REGISTER VOL. 36, NUMBER 105,
SATURDAY, MAY 29, 1971

CHAPTER TEN
Target Health Hazards Program

ASBESTOS

WHAT IS IT?

Asbestos is a general term used to describe several fibrous mineral silicates that occur as white, grayish or greenish masses, either compact or of long silky fibers. The most important types are Chrysolite®, a simple magnesium silicate; amosite, a complex magnesium iron silicate; and crocidolite, a complex sodium iron silicate. Some 95% of world asbestos production comes from Chrysolite.

WHERE IS IT?

The heat-resistant properties of asbestos have led to many uses, for example, protection against fire, insulation, brake and clutch linings, building materials, filters and in plastics. The raw material and end-products are found nearly everywhere.

WHAT IS THE HAZARD?

More than 200,000 employees face risks from asbestos. The principal danger is caused by inhaling asbestos fibers. Recent studies have shown the presence of asbestos fibers in the lungs of persons having no industrial exposure, probably due to their presence in the atmosphere near construction sites. Prolonged inhalation of asbestos fibers between 5 and 50 microns long (one-millionth of a meter) can produce a lung disease known as asbestosis. The lungs cannot eliminate asbestos fibers, so the fibers coat the tissues. If this process continues over a period of 10 to 20 years, with significant quantities of asbestos present, the tissue reaction progresses until a generalized, diffuse fibrosis occurs, causing severe respiratory disability. There have been reports of increased incidence of lung cancer in persons with asbestosis.

HOW IS IT CONTROLLED?

Enclosure and local exhaust ventilation applied to equipment and/or operations are the principal means of preventing employee exposure to dangerously high concentrations. The U. S. Bureau of Mines states that approved dust respirators may be worn by employees as protection for some operations.

WHAT ARE APPROVED LEVELS?

OSHA's permissible level is five fibers per milliliter greater than five microns in length for an eight-hour, time-weighted, average airborne concentration. This may be increased to 10 such fibers per milliliter for no more than 15 minutes per hour, up to five hours per eight-hour day. Imminent danger situations are generally not applicable. Any exposure greater than permissible levels for unprotected or improperly protected workers is considered a serious violation.

HOW IS IT MEASURED?

Asbestos dust will be collected with a personal sampling pump. Fibers will be counted microscopically at 400-450 magnification using phase contrast illumination.

CARBON MONOXIDE

WHAT IS IT?

Carbon monoxide is a colorless, almost odorless, tasteless, non-irritating gas. It is produced by the incomplete combustion of fuels, such as wood, gas, coal, oil and gasoline. Miners refer to it as "white damp." It also is commonly called "coal gas."

WHERE IS IT?

Carbon monoxide is found anywhere carbonaceous fuels are used. It can be found in everyday activities as well as in industrial situations, near incorrectly vented gas heaters, near gasoline-powered machinery and around automobiles run indoors, blast furnaces, and catalytic reduction operations.

WHAT IS THE HAZARD?

Because it is found so widely, nearly everyone, at one time or another, is exposed to carbon monoxide. The danger lies in inhalation of the gas. Carbon monoxide enters the blood stream through the lungs in the same manner as oxygen, but it displaces oxygen in the blood because it has approximately 210 times greater affinity for hemoglobin in the blood than oxygen. As a result, the blood cannot transport oxygen, causing suffocation even in an atmosphere containing ample oxygen. Over a period of time, as little as 700 parts per million of carbon monoxide will saturate 50% of the blood hemoglobin, while a few breaths at concentrations of 10,000 parts per million may cause 60 to 80% saturation and death. Fortunately, regardless of how high the percentage of saturation of the blood has been, practically all carbon monoxide is eliminated by the body within 8 to 10 hours after exposure ends.

HOW IS IT CONTROLLED?

In general, adequate ventilation will prevent carbon monoxide poisoning. Enclosure, general or dilution ventilation and local exhaust ventilation, as well as isolation of hazardous operations are the principal means of preventing employee exposure to dangerous concentrations. Automated detection alarm systems also are useful control measures.

WHAT ARE APPROVED LEVELS?

OSHA's permissible level is 50 parts per million parts of air for an eight-hour, time-weighted, average airborne concentration. Concentrations above 500 parts per million for any length of time are considered to be imminent danger situations. Concentrations above 150 parts per million for a total of one hour or more are considered to be serious violations. Concentrations above 50 parts per million, but below 150 parts per million, for an eight-hour, time-weighted average are considered regular or nonserious violations.

HOW IS IT MEASURED?

The primary method of measurement is a carbon monoxide portable, Hopcalite-reagent type meter. The secondary method is certified detector tubes.

COTTON DUST

WHERE IS IT?

Cotton dust occurs throughout the textile industry and affects cotton, flax and soft hemp workers. The greatest exposure to cotton dust generally occurs during the carding of cotton, an operation that combs out cotton fibers and sets them parallel by drawing them between toothed cylinders. However, machinery throughout the cotton mill must be cleaned frequently, and much exposure to cotton dust occurs then.

WHAT IS THE HAZARD?

More than 800,000 employees in cotton processing operations of all types are exposed to cotton dust. While the exact effects of cotton dust are not known, prolonged exposure to heavy air concentrations can cause a disabling lung disease known as byssinosis. Materials adhering to cotton fibers, such as unwanted leaf, stem and boll trash, when inhaled, elicit an allergic reaction or response. Byssinosis generally advances through three recognizable stages. The first is commonly called "Monday fever" and begins only after exposure of more than 10 years. Workers develop an irritating cough, tightness of the chest and breathlessness. The attacks usually come on Monday, or after a period of absence from the plant and last only a day or so; hence the name "Monday fever." In the second stage, these symptoms extend over more days in the week and finally become permanent. If exposure to cotton dust is ended at this stage, recovery can occur. In the third stage, the tightness of the chest and labored breathing become so distressing the worker must leave the industry. The disease can progress then to chronic bronchitis and emphysema.

HOW IS IT CONTROLLED?

Enclosure of machinery in all operations and local exhaust ventilation are the principal means of preventing employee exposure. Pretreatment of the cotton in early processing stages may also be helpful.

WHAT ARE APPROVED LEVELS?

OSHA's permissible level is one milligram per cubic meter of air for an eight-hour, time-weighted, average airborne concentration. Imminent danger situations are generally not applicable. Concentrations of three milligrams per cubic meter are considered serious violations; concentrations between one and three milligrams per cubic meter for an eight-hour, time-weighted average are considered regular or nonserious violations.

HOW IS IT MEASURED?

A personal sampler is attached to a workman's clothing with the uncovered filter facing down. Usually a six hour sample is obtained.

LEAD

WHAT IS IT?
Lead is a soft, dense, malleable, heavy metal with a low melting point. It is gray in color and, because of its characteristics, has a wide application of uses.

WHERE IS IT?
Lead is used to make printing type and plumbing, to shield telephone and power cables and to protect against radiation hazards. As an alloy, lead mixed with steel makes excellent bearings. As solder, lead alloy is vital in the electrical and electronic industries. Lead compounds are used to make paints and ammunition, and lead oxides are used in car batteries.

WHAT IS THE HAZARD?
More than 1.6 million employees in nearly every industrial manufacturing process and in many service industries are exposed to the poisoning effect of lead. Lead can enter the body by inhalation, absorption through the skin or by ingestion. In sufficient quantities, the result is the same—severe gastrointestinal, blood and central nervous system disorders. Inhalation of lead dust or fumes is the most frequent means of entry and results in most of the industrial health problems involving this metal. Because lead is a cumulative poison, a part of a small daily dose is not eliminated but is stored in the body. Eventually, a point is reached where symptoms and disability, even death, occur.

HOW IS IT CONTROLLED?
Since the primary route of industrial lead poisoning is inhalation, enclosure and local exhaust ventilation are the principal means of control. Daily wet or vacuum cleaning of all lead dust, personal hygiene, prohibition of food and beverages in the work area and use of U. S. Bureau of Mines-approved respirators are other means that can help control exposure.

WHAT ARE APPROVED LEVELS?
OSHA's permissible level is 0.2 milligrams per cubic meter of air for an eight-hour, time-weighted, average airborne concentration. Imminent danger situations are not generally applicable. Any exposure above 0.6 milligrams per cubic meter of air for an eight-hour, time-weighted average is considered a serious violation. Levels above 0.2 and less than 0.6 are considered regular or nonserious violations.

HOW IS IT MEASURED?

The sample is collected for a minimum of 60 minutes by a personal sampling pump on a millipore filter. The filter is subsequently dissolved in nitric acid by taking the lead into solution. The solution is then introduced into an atomic absorption unit for analysis.

SILICA

WHAT IS IT?

Silica is an oxide of silicon and is the characteristic ingredient of a great variety of minerals, including quartz, cristobalite, tridymite, amethyst and sand. It is widely used in cores for metal casting operations, ceramics, decorative materials, insulation, building materials and glass.

WHERE IS IT?

Silica is found throughout industry in various manufacturing processes, such as iron and mineral processing plants, mining, abrasive soap production, glass manufacturing, potteries, foundries, abrasives use and manufacturing, in stone cutting and finishing industries.

WHAT IS THE HAZARD?

More than 1.1 million employees are exposed to the hazard created by inhalation of silica dust. Inhalation of these particles can produce rapidly-developing (acute) or chronic silicosis, a disabling lung disease. Typically, the lung tissue reacts to the presence of silica particles by forming fibrous matter around the particle. Evidence suggests that particles below one micron (one-millionth of a meter) in size may be the most dangerous, since they may penetrate deeper into the lungs in high concentrations. In rapidly developing silicosis, symptoms appear eight to 18 months after the first exposure. Chronic silicosis, the type usually encountered in industry, generally is produced only after years of silica inhalation. The symptoms for either type are the same—slowly increasing difficulty in breathing under exertion. In some workers, large masses of dense fibrous tissue develop in the upper portion of the lungs, leading to severe respiratory crippling. Tuberculosis is a frequent complication of silicosis.

HOW IS IT CONTROLLED?

The best method is substitution of another material; for example, use of steel shot or alumina grit in place of sandblasting operations. Other methods include enclosure of operations, local exhaust ventilation, segregation of operations, wetting, and ordinary good-housekeeping practices.

WHAT ARE APPROVED LEVELS?

For respirable quartz particles, OSHA's permissible level is 10 milligrams per cubic meter of air, divided by the percent of free silica plus 2, as shown in this formula: $\dfrac{10mg/m^3}{\%SiO_2+2}$.

For respirable cristobalite and tridymite, the limits are half the value for quartz. Imminent danger situations generally are not applicable. Any eight-hour, time-weighted average greater than four times the limit is considered a serious violation. Exposure to concentrations between the limit and four times the limit are considered a regular or nonserious violation.

HOW IS IT MEASURED?

Personal sampling pumps with filters are used to collect dust samples for worker exposure. The collected dust then is weighed for a given volume of air. Similar procedures are used to determine the percentage of silica in the air.

CHAPTER ELEVEN
NIOSH

Section 22 of the Act creates a National Institute of Occupational Safety and Health (NIOSH) in the Department of Health, Education and Welfare (HEW) to carry out Congressional policy, as set forth in Section 2 of the Act, to develop and establish recommended occupational safety and health standards, and to perform the research, training and other functions of the Secretary of Health, Education and Welfare delineated in Sections 20 and 21 of the Act.

The establishment of the Institute is intended to "elevate the status of occupational health and safety research to place it on equal footing with the research conducted by HEW into other matters of vital social concern."

In addressing an AFL-CIO conference on the Occupational Safety and Health Act, Dr. Marcus Key, first Director of the Bureau of Occupational Safety and Health, in HEW, outlined the organizational structure, functions and responsibilities of the new structure.

FUNCTIONAL ORGANIZATION

NIOSH is organized functionally, rather than along disciplinary lines. There are operating divisions for each major activity. For health and safety research there is the Division of Laboratories and Criteria; for industry-wide studies the Division of Field Studies and Clinical Investigation; for hazard evaluations the Division of Technical Services; and for short-term training the Division of Training.

These four divisions operate out of Cincinnati, Salt Lake City, and the regional offices. Their directors report to an Associate Director in Cincinnati who reports to the Director in Washington. The Appalachian Laboratory for Occupational Respiratory Diseases in Morgantown has the sole responsibility for implementing the Coal Mine Health and Safety Act.

A division in Washington promotes occupational health programs at the Federal and state levels as well as in industry and agriculture. This division also has the very important responsibility of correlating the practice of occupational medicine in industry with the total delivery of health services. Other offices in Washington that interface with the Department of Labor include the Office of Health Surveillance and Biometrics, the Office of Manpower Development, and the Office of Research and Standards Development.

NIOSH technical services operations are decentralized and operate on the regional basis, similar to OSHA function and structure.

Plans for the end of 1972 were to staff regional offices with two professionals—a program director and an assistant and a secretary. Original staffing was estimated on the basis of the expected number of requests for hazards evaluations and in all probability will be increased.

Monitoring and surveillance activities are also part of the NIOSH regional office function. The office employs industrial hygienist surveyors who conduct preliminary surveys to gather information on the industrial hygiene problems in the United States. Regional offices also provide assistance on State plans, contract and grant monitoring, training and recruitment.

HEW RESPONSIBILITIES

The major responsibilities of HEW, according to Dr. Key, are these: health and safety research, industry-wide studies, hazard evaluations, toxicity determinations, annual listing of toxic substances, record-keeping, and manpower development and training.

Of the many different types of research which are authorized for HEW, the most important is that which produces criteria on which standards for toxic materials and harmful physical agents can be based. The criteria which HEW will transmit to the Department of Labor will contain not only all pertinent dose-effect studies with literature citations, but also specific limit recommendations based on health effects.

Feasibility studies are performed to produce a manual of good practices for each substance, with the Department of Labor adding items relating to the national interest and economic considerations for publishing proposed standards, and for public hearings if necessary.

"HEW," Dr. Key said, "has had considerable experience in this type of health research, but we have a big task ahead of us in tooling up for safety research. In this area we plan to emphasize motivational and behavioral factors in safety, ergonomics and work physiology."

NIOSH is charged, within two years of its inception and annually thereafter, with conducting and publishing industry-wide studies on the effect of chronic and low-level industrial exposures which may have potential for disease or physical impairment.

The asbestos, beryllium, cotton dust and noise studies first undertaken by NIOSH are examples of the prescribed industry-wide studies. These environmental-medical studies will increase and many different types of studies and records will be added as NIOSH looks for long-term effects and for causes of shortened life span.

TOXICITY RULINGS

NIOSH is required to make hazard evaluations and toxicity determinations when a request in writing is made by any employer or group of employees. Estimates at the outset of the program were that there would be 5,000 such requests a year.

The requests will be received through regional offices which have access to a computerized technical information system. In this system are stored trade name, composition, toxicity data, sampling and analytical procedures, and suggested limits, if any.

If the request concerns a substance for which there is already a standard, it is referred to the Department of Labor. Otherwise a field visit by an industrial hygienist from NIOSH is made. Anticipation is that final determination can be made on the first visit for about half of the requests, field sampling on a return visit for some 25%, and the remainder, in the area of almost complete unknowns, will require acute, subacute and chronic toxicity studies. Medical studies may also be indicated.

If there are more requests than can be handled, priorities will be established based on the severity of risk and numbers of people exposed.

The annual compilation of toxic substances will identify each substance by generic name, will give the known toxic concentration which has most application to man under conditions of occupational exposure, and will contain literature citations. For many substances there will be no human data and it will be necessary to supply animal data with the closest approximation to the industrial route of exposure given.

The definition of toxicity is broad, including carcinogens (cancer-producing), mutagens (change-producing) and teratogens (monster-producing). Estimates are that some 12,000 items will comprise the first list, compared with the 400-500 substances for which TLV's (threshold limit values) or standards are available. This is considered to be NIOSH's "shopping list" for standards setting. Later lists will be longer and contain much more information.

Record keeping will be required (of employers) by the Department of Labor, and in some cases, HEW. HEW requests, however, will be made through the Department of Labor so as not to confuse or overwhelm industry. In the development of the record keeping and reporting system NIOSH has worked with the Department of Labor and ANSI (American National Standards Institute). Occupational illnesses will be reported for the first time, and will be broken down into several major categories.

EDUCATIONAL PROGRAMS

One of NIOSH's principal responsibilities is the development of educational programs to provide an adequate supply of qualified personnel to carry out the purposes of the Act. Such trainees would be utilized by the Department of Labor, the Department of HEW, other Federal agencies, state health and labor departments, business, industry and political subdivisions.

Implementation of the manpower responsibility includes many different programs. Through short courses, NIOSH says, and the associated extern programs in industry and state occupational safety and health agencies, it will train high school graduates to be technicians, junior college graduates to be para-professionals, and college graduates to be occupational safety and health professionals.

NIOSH seeks to increase the number of occupational safety and health professionals, para-professionals and technicians through
1. two to four year college program support
2. nursing school support for a last year option in occupational health nursing
3. masters level graduate training
4. research training grants.

Dr. Key stated, and experience to date tends to bear him out, that the health aspects of the Act will overshadow the safety aspects, and that HEW responsibilities are much more difficult than DOL responsibilities.

Enforcement, he said, is relatively easy when the limit is given and the sampling method and analytical procedures are specified. The greater challenge and responsibility lies in trail blazing or ascertaining if there is a health hazard, programming criteria or dose-effect type research to set a standard, and determining the limit which offers the greatest health protection.

ADMINISTRATIVE RESPONSIBILITY

According to its organizational statement NIOSH assumes responsibility for:

1. administering health and safety research, including studies of psychological factors pertaining to employment health and safety,

2. developing innovative methods and approaches for dealing with job-related safety and health problems,

3. providing medical criteria to provide, "insofar as practicable, that no employee will suffer diminished life expectancy as a result of his work experience," to develop methods of recognizing latent diseases and to isolate causal relationships between diseases and working conditions,

4. contributing to the development of training programs to increase the numbers and competence of safety and health personnel,

5. developing reporting procedures to aid in describing the nature of the nation's safety and health problems, and,

6. consulting with the U. S. Department of Labor, other federal, state and local government agencies, labor and management groups, and others interested in the promotion of occupational safety and health.

Administrative responsibility for these activities has been divided among eight main offices and several operating divisions within the National Institute. The principal divisions and duties are described below.

OFFICE OF THE DIRECTOR

This office (1) plans, directs, coordinates, and evaluates the operations of the institute, (2) maintains liaison with and provides advice and assistance to the U.S. Department of Labor, the U.S. Department of the Interior, other Federal agencies, state and local government agencies, international health organizations, and outside groups, (3) provides coordination with the Federal Health Programs Service's occupational health activities for Federal employees, and (4) provides policy guidance and coordination to occupational safety and health activities in the Regional Offices.

OFFICE OF PUBLIC INFORMATION

This office (1) assists and advises the Institute Director and the Divisions on public information policies and activities, (2) provides information materials for response to public inquiries, (3) coordinates printing, publication, and clearance procedures for the Institute, and (4) assists in developing displays, exhibits, and illustrations.

OFFICE OF EXTRAMURAL ACTIVITIES

This office (1) advises the Institute Director on matters relating to the development and progress of Institute-supported external research, (2) in cooperation with the offices and operating divisions of the Institute, stimulates research, training, and demonstration grants in relevant priority areas, and (3) administers the management aspects of the Institute's grants programs by receiving, reviewing, analyzing, and evaluating all grant applications.

OFFICE OF ADMINISTRATIVE MANAGEMENT

This office (1) provides management information, advice, and guidance to the Institute Director, (2) coordinates all management activities in the conduct of finance, personnel, and procurement functions, (3) relates administrative management activities to programs, and (4) develops necessary policies, procedures, and operations, and provides such special reports and studies as may be required in the management area.

OFFICE OF PLANNING AND RESOURCE MANAGEMENT

This office (1) plans and coordinates the strategy and philosophy of operation of the Institute regarding mission and objectives, (2) conducts or participates in special studies for program planning and evaluation, (3) conducts the necessary control functions to assure operational compliance toward program objectives within the Institute, and (4) provides management systems consultation and analyses.

OFFICE OF RESEARCH AND STANDARDS DEVELOPMENT

This office (1) reviews existing scientific criteria for health and safety standards and assesses through priority systems the needs for additional research program areas for criteria development, and (2) coordinates and maintains an overview of research activities in the operating divisions of the Institute with the ultimate aim toward finalization of criteria and standards.

OFFICE OF MANPOWER DEVELOPMENT

This office (1) provides policy guidance and evaluates the Institute's manpower development and training activities, (2) advises the Institute Director on national health manpower needs related to occupational safety and health, and relates to other Federal agencies regarding occupational safety and health manpower needs, and (3) conducts equal employment opportunity activities of the Institute as part of the total HSMHA-EEO program.

OFFICE OF HEALTH SURVEILLANCE AND BIOMETRICS

This office (1) operates as the principal statistical and data research unit in the Institute, (2) monitors new as well as existing occupational hazards, and maintains surveillance on the incidence of occupational illnesses and diseases, (3) in coordination with the U. S. Department of Labor, establishes a priority list for the conduct of research and the development of standards, (4) develops and conducts record studies of work population groups to determine the national trends and problem areas related to job health and safety, and provides health policy guidance in epidemiology, and (5) coordinates the Institute's electronic data processing requirements, to ensure that adequate computer facilities and services are available.

DIVISION OF LABORATORIES AND CRITERIA DEVELOPMENT

This office (1) develops criteria for standards for the control of chemical, biological, and physical hazards to the health and safety of the working population, and initiates standard methodology and instrumentation for the detection, evaluation, and control of such hazards, (2) evaluates the toxicity, health, and safety hazards of industrial substances, processes, and other agents, as well as current research requirements and regulations, (3) conducts methodology studies for evaluating the varying capacity of workers to withstand physical and psychological responses, (4) provides for equipment development, analytical service, and calibration needs of other operating divisions within the Institute, and maintains an analytical and calibrations service for the U. S. Department of Labor, and (5) evaluates and certifies the performance of safety and health equipment.

DIVISION OF FIELD STUDIES AND CLINICAL INVESTIGATORS

This division (1) conducts nation-wide studies, surveys and comprehensive analyses to determine the health status of the working population, including the incidence and prevalence of disease and injury, and (2) initiates studies to determine chronic and long-term effects of work-related exposures to toxic and hazardous sub-stances.

DIVISION OF TECHNICAL SERVICES

This division (1) provides demonstrations, technical assistance, and consultation to public and private agencies responsible for the control of occupational diseases and accidental work injuries, (2) through the Regional Offices and its central staff serves as the focal point for the review of state plans and grants with the U. S. Department of Labor and makes the initial responses to requests for hazards evaluations, (3) in cooperation with the Office of Extramural Activities, stimulates, programs, and monitors demonstration grants for new and innovative methods of recognizing, evaluating, and controlling occupational hazards, (4) prepares manuals of good practice for safe work procedures, and (5) operates the technical information inquiry service of the Institute.

DIVISION OF OCCUPATIONAL HEALTH PROGRAMS

This division (1) promotes occupational health programs at the state and local governmental levels as well as in industry and agriculture, (2) provides technical guidance in the development of occupational health programs, and (3) correlates the practice of occupational medicine in industry with the total delivery of health services.

DIVISION OF TRAINING

This division (1) develops and plans short-term training activities for Federal, state, and local governments, industry, and other appropriate organizations in the field of occupational safety and health, and (2) conducts such short-term training.

APPALACHIAN LABORATORY FOR OCCUPATIONAL RESPIRATORY DISEASES

The laboratory (1) conducts studies of the incidences and prevalence of occupational respiratory diseases in specific work groups with particular emphasis on coal workers' pneumoconiosis, and (2) provides medical and engineering research and service to fulfill the Institute's responsibilities under the Federal Coal Mine Health and Safety Act of 1969.

1972 PRIORITY LIST FOR CRITERIA FOR TOXIC SUBSTANCES AND PHYSICAL AGENTS

The following list was designed to help researchers identify areas where criteria information is needed. Five weighted indices were

assigned to each substance under consideration. They were rated on a scale of 9 to 1 and included the following:
1. Population Index (PI): a relative evaluation of worker exposure
2. Relative Toxicity Index (RT): professional opinion on relative toxicity
3. Incidence Index (II): occupational disease records, physicians' first reports, workmen's compensation records, and other documented incidents of disease
4. Quantity Index (QI): amount produced or used each year
5. Trend Index (TI): estimates on increased or decreased usage.
The overall rating for each substance was computed using the formula: 2PI + 2RT + II + QI + TI divided by 5.

NATIONAL INSTITUTE FOR OCCUPATIONAL SAFETY AND HEALTH PRIORITY LIST FOR CRITERIA FOR TOXIC SUBSTANCES AND PHYSICAL AGENTS, 1972

Criteria have been developed for asbestos and coal dust. Substances for which criteria are still being developed are arsenic, benzene, beryllium, cadmium and compounds, carbon monoxide, chromic acid mist, cotton dust, fibrous glass, heat stress, lead, mercury, noise, parathion, silica, trichloroethylene, and ultraviolet.

PRIORITIES
1.
Bis (chloromethyl) ether
Coal tar pitch volatiles
2-Naphthylamine
Toluene diisocyanate
Radioactive products of uranium mining (gaseous and particulate)
2.
Benzidine and its salts
Carbon Tetrachloride
Ozone
Sulfur dioxide
Tin and compounds
3.
Chromium compounds
Dichlorobenzidine
Oxides of nitrogen
Sodium hydroxide
Sulfuric acid

4.
Carbaryl
Chloroform
4-Dimethylaminoazobenzene
Nitric acid
Toluene
5.
Ammonia
Beta-propiolactone
Epoxy resins
Methylene chloride
4-nitrodiphenyl
6.
Asphalt fumes
Ethylene dichloride
Fluoride and HF
Polychlorinated biphenyls
Tetrachloroethylene
7.
2-Acetylaminofluorene

Chlorobenzene
Methylene bisphenyl isocyanate
(MDI)
Phosgene
Trichloroethane
8.
Acetone
4-Aminodiphenyl
Dieldrin
Malathion
N-nitrosodimethylamine
9.
Aniline
Copper and compounds
Cyanides
Styrene
Zinc and compounds
10.
Chlorine
Formaldehyde
Manganese and compounds
Phenol
Platinum and compounds
11.
Acrolein
Aluminum and compounds
Carbon disulfide
Methyl ethyl ketone
Vinyl chloride
12.
Creosote
Methyl chloride
Nickel and compounds
Phosphorus and compounds
Tetrachloroethane
13.
Acrylonitrile
2,4-Dinitrophenol
Magnesium and compounds

Methyl alcohol
Paraffin
14.
Ammonium nitrate
Cold stress
Dioxane
Flourine
Microwaves
15.
Hydrogen chloride
Ethyl benzene
Nitroglycerin
Vibration
Xylene
16.
Methyl butyl ketone
Mineral spirits
Oil mists
Selenium and compounds
Turpentine
17.
Arsine
Gasoline
Kerosene
Iron and compounds
Petroleum naphtha
18.
Barotrauma
Cresol
Paraquat
Portland cement
Talc
19.
Carbon black
Coherent energy (laser radi-
ation)
Ethylene oxide
Impact noise
Proteolytic enzymes

NATIONAL SURVEILLANCE NETWORK
NATIONAL OCCUPATIONAL HAZARD SURVEY FORM

This is included in the text to give employers and employees some specific idea of the scope and function of NIOSH and the importance attributed to the "health" side of the Occupational Safety and Health Act of 1970.

1. Facility name
2. Address
3. City, state, zip code
4. Legal Owner(s)
5. Person(s) interviewed: name, title, part
6. Area code, telephone
7. Date survey started or visit made
8. Facility identifier
   If mailing address or person to contact concerning information about the survey is different from that indicated above, list the correct mailing and contact below.
9. Facility name
10. Address
11. City, state, zip code
12. Attention: title
13. Area code, telephone

Facility Health and Safety Services
1. Revision code
2. Date survey started (month/day/year)
3. State code
4. Facility identifier code
5. Area of business
   a. What is your major activity?
   b. What are your chief products, services, lines of trade, etc.?
   c. SIC code if known.
6. Approximately how many years has this facility been involved in this activity?
7. How many people are on your facility payroll for all shifts at the present time?
8. Of this number, how many are normally in the work areas as opposed to the administrative or other areas?
9. How many shifts do you have?
10. Has this facility received industrial hygiene services during the past year?

Yes, from an industrial hygienist   (1)
Yes, from a safety engineer   (2)
   (Skip to Question 13)
Yes, from other. Specify: (3)
   (Skip to Question 13)
No   (Skip to Question 13)   (4)

11. Is the industrial hygienist based in this facility?
Yes   (1)

No, consulting basis   (3)
No, other. Specify: (4)
Not applicable   (5)

12. Estimate the average number of industrial hygienist hours that are devoted to your facility per month.

13. Has your facility received safety engineer services during the past year?
Yes, from a safety engineer based in this facility   (1)
Yes, from a safety engineer based elsewhere   (2)
Yes, on a consulting basis   (3)
Yes, other. Specify: (4)
No   (5)

14. Estimate the average number of safety engineer hours that are devoted to your facility per month.

15. Is there a formally established health unit at this facility?
Yes, physician in charge   (1)
Yes, Registered Nurse in charge   (2)
Yes, Licensed Practical Nurse in charge   (3)
Yes, other in charge. Specify: (4)
No   (5)

16. Do you employ or have an arrangement with a physician or clinic to give your employees medical care?
Yes, employed full time   (1)
Yes, employed part time   (2)
Yes, on call   (Skip to Question 18)   (3)
Yes, at clinic   (Skip to Question 18)   (4)
Other. Specify: (Skip to Question 18)   (5)
No arrangements made   (Skip to Question 18)   (6)

17. Estimate the average number of physician hours that are devoted to your facility per week.

18. Do you have one or more nurses at this facility to provide care for employees?
Yes   (1)
No (Question 19—not applicable)   (2)

19. How many Registered Nurses and Licensed Practical Nurses are employed at this facility?

20. Estimate the average number of nursing hours that are devoted to your facility per week.

21. Do you have an employee at this facility with formal first-aid training, other than doctors or nurses, who has been designated to provide emergency treatment?

Yes   (1)
No   (2)

22. Do you record health information about a new employee on some regular form?

Yes, all employees   (1)
Yes, executive and/or managerial only   (2)
Yes, other employees   (3)
No   (4)

23. Before new employees are hired or placed, are they required to take a medical examination?

Yes, all employees   (1)
Yes, executive and/or managerial only   (2)
Yes, other employees   (3)
No   (4)

24. Do you require medical examinations of your employees who return to work after a sickness, or whose employment is terminated?

Return to work only   (1)
Exit examination at time of termination only   (2)
Both   (3)
Neither   (4)

25. Do you provide periodic medical examinations or tests of any type for employees?

Yes, all employees   (1)
Yes, executive and/or managerial only   (2)
Yes, other employees   (3)
No   (4)

26. Do you provide periodic ophthalmologic examinations for employees?

Yes, all employees   (1)
Yes, executive and/or managerial only   (2)
Yes, other employees   (3)
No   (4)

27. Do you provide periodic audiometric examinations for employees?

Yes, all employees   (1)

Yes, executive and/or managerial only   (2)
Yes, other employees   (3)
No   (4)

28. Do you provide periodic blood tests for employees?
Yes, all employees   (1)
Yes, executive and/or managerial only   (2)
Yes, other employees   (3)
No   (4)

29. Do you provide periodic urine tests for employees?
Yes, all employees   (1)
Yes, executive and/or managerial only   (2)
Yes, other employees   (3)
No   (4)

30. Do you provide periodic pulmonary function tests for employees?
Yes, all employees   (1)
Yes, executive and/or managerial only   (2)
Yes, other employees   (3)
No   (4)

31. Do you provide periodic chest X-rays for employees?
Yes, all employees   (1)
Yes, executive and/or managerial only   (2)
Yes, other employees   (3)
No   (4)

32. Do you have a regularly scheduled program to give employees flu, cold, or other immunizations?
Yes   (1)
No   (2)

33. Do you keep employee absenteeism records?
Yes, showing specific nature of sickness when absent   (1)
Yes, showing only the type of absence   (2)
Yes, without showing nature of absence   (3)
No   (4)

34. What is your rate of unscheduled absenteeism (days per year per employee)?

35. Is there a formally established safety committee at your facility?
Yes, investigative   (1)
Yes, policy setting   (2)
Both   (3)
Yes, other. Specify: (e.g. advisory only)   (4)
No   (5)

36. Do you have areas where personal protective devices are required or recommended?

Yes, required	(1)
Yes, recommended	(2)
Yes, both	(3)
No	(4)

37. Who provides personal protective devices?

Employee	(1)
Employer	(2)
Both	(3)
Other. Specify:	(4)
Not applicable	(5)

38. Who has been designated to see to it that personal protective devices are serviced and maintained?

Individual employees	(1)
Employer representative	(2)
Both	(3)
Other. Specify:	(4)
No one	(5)
Not applicable	(6)

39. How do you carry your workmen's compensation insurance?

Private insurance company	(1)
Self-insured	(2)
State insurance fund	(3)
Other. Specify:	(4)
None	(5)

40. Are any unions operating in this facility?

Yes	(1)
No	(2)

41. Is this facility a member of a national association or institute representing its industry or trade?

Yes	(1)
No	(2)

42. Do you have a program under which you regularly monitor the presence of fumes, gases, mists, vapors, dusts, noise, vibration, radiation or other similar conditions?

Yes	(1)
No	(2)

43. Do you use a private sewage treatment plant or a septic tank to dispose of this facility's nonprocess sewage?

Yes, private sewage treatment plant	(1)
Yes, septic tank	(2)

Yes, both   (3)

No   (4)

44. Do you have any drinking water other than that provided through a public water supply?

Yes. Specify: (1)

No   (2)

45. Is the private water supply routinely tested for bacteriological quality?

Yes   (1)

No   (2)

Not applicable   (3)

46. Do you have any piped liquids other than drinking water?

Yes. Specify: (1)

No   (2)

47. Is there a separate, identified eating area for your work area employees?

Yes   (1)

No   (2)

48. Are hand washing facilities provided within 200 feet of the eating area?

Yes   (1)

No   (2)

Not applicable   (3)

49. May I see the Summary of Occupational Injuries and Illnesses (OSHA Form 102)?

Occupational injuries

Occupational illnesses

Occupational skin diseases or disorders

Dust diseases of the lungs (pneumoconioses)

Respiratory conditions due to toxic materials

Poisoning (systemic effects of toxic materials)

Disorder due to physical agents (other than toxic materials)

Disorders due to repeated trauma

All other occupational illnesses. Specify:

50. How many months are covered by the preceding figures?

CHAPTER TWELVE
Conclusion

The Act, of course, poses business, industry and political subdivision problems. Certainly it adds to the numbers of regulatory mandates which business claims makes the profit-making process more and more difficult. The truth of this is difficult to assess.

The Act's necessity, however, just like traffic laws or other regulations in our overall group and individual interest, seems unquestionable. It seems fairly self-evident that with the lack of safety and health laws of any description in some states, with fair laws in others, and even with good laws lacking ordinances for enforcement, or finding those ordinances not implemented—that something had to happen with sufficient national impact to put environmental occupational protection in proper perspective.

The Williams-Steiger Occupational Safety and Health Act of 1970 is a good beginning, but it gave some indication in its first year of implementation of being a political document, subject to the winds of change that such documents incur.

The Act, its language, intent and purpose is noble and majestic in tone, objective and ideal, and is, in fact, long overdue. What we do with it here in the U. S. is of concern to those who have invested their lifetime, their talent, their ambition and whatever dedication they could manage, to the proposition that the working man and woman has every right to expect that life on the job should be free (not as much as "feasible" or "practicable," but as much as possible) from injury, death or illness.

It remains to be seen whether a vested interest group, and labor is no different than employer in this area, pulls the teeth of what began as a healthy jawful of molars, grinders and incisors. Some *visits to the dentist* have already occurred.

The closest thing to a real representative for the average shift worker, hard-hat, blue collar or clock puncher—the individual who gets the job done—is not the union nor the employer. It is the Federal government when it enacts the kind of legislation represented by the Williams-Steiger Occupational Safety and Health Act of 1970.

The employee stands between a rock and a hard place when these two giants argue and negotiate over his welfare or lack of it, what is best for him and what isn't. Decisions that can make the difference between what is really a safe and healthful practice or place to work and what is not can find their way no farther than a review committee, a criteria package, a covert or overt power play, a politician seeking re-election with numerous "obligations" to repay, before they disappear into oblivion.

The Act makes this possibility more difficult, but there have been some alarming back-offs in the face of all that brave and wonderful wordage, and the tendency to use the *weasel words* is still prevalent.

The Act's biggest problem, however, in terms of securing its stated objectives, is not political. It is educational. It is securing and training personnel in numbers and capability to effectively manage this new responsibility. Involved as we have been in developing a training and education program for the University of Puget Sound, our observation is that the answer is not the Act itself but the people responsible for its leadership in the workplace. The supply of such trained personnel is woefully short and will be for some time.

The reason, of course, is the limbo in which something vaguely defined, known and shelved as "safety" has found itself for years. If "safety" was relegated to that position, such sophisticates as "Occupational Health" and "Industrial Hygiene" were even lesser known.

Seventy per cent of today's industry, companies who hire less than 100 employes, still know little about the Act and much less about NIOSH, or what industrial hygiene or occupational health has to do with them.

NIOSH, as we noted, faced with the responsibility of "education and manpower development," is adding training programs. HEW is supporting occupational safety and health curriculi with federal funding, as colleges and universities for the first time are developing and presenting training programs to meet a need which has been there for a long time.

In the press and rush to meet this need, there is a tendency to simply cram a curriculum together and start teaching it. HEW funding requirements, as a matter of fact, make it virtually impossible to *develop* a curriculum. If a college, university or institute is seeking federal funds to initiate an environmental occupational protection curriculum, in order to qualify for such funding the curriculum must be already completely determined—courses, subject matter, credit hours, etc. This has some inherent and built-in handicaps. First of all, from any logical viewpoint, a curriculum has to be *developed*, particularly a new one. It needs to be developed to meet the need, not the pragmatic specification of some one or some group who says that curriculum meets the need.

Today's occupational safety and health requirements, rules and regulations, posture, attitude, philosophy, objectives and goals, is a new ball game. Stereotyped, standard, traditional inflexibilities need their clanking machinery unlocked. New definitions, new wordage, new application, and new horizons are needed. Such words as "safety" and "accident" need to be changed, redefined, or eliminated. Occupational safety and occupational health need to become a partnership rather than two separate and competing disciplines.

The real, immediate and urgent training need is not two-year, four-year, or graduate level degree programs. It is short-course training for the man or woman faced with the new responsibility of coping with OSHA—1970. He needs competent, capable, instruction directly related to the Act and its requirements.

Such courses need to be developed in subject matter and time-span so they can be applied for later credit within a two-year or four-year or graduate degree program. Out of such development and experience an intelligent, practical and working curriculum can be developed.

While federal funding of such projects leaves much to be desired, the plain and simple fact is that any curriculum to be successful must be self-sustaining. Curricula already set in concrete tends to follow a lead set in "safety" in years preceding the passage of the Act, years singularly unsuccessful in any noteworthy achievement other than holding the line. Also today's "professional" is still sitting on his hands, waiting for someone else to take the lead, is still doing someone else's bidding, is still looking to management for approval before making any kind of move.

In terms of opportunity to do a better and more professional environmental occupation protection job, fast-developing and broadening responsibility, and status and income, the occupational safety and health director never had it so good.

What we need today is a man or woman who tells management what it could and should be doing, sells them on doing it and then gets the job done. We don't need followers or expedient or political operators in the field of environmental occupational protection; we need capable, tough-minded, innovative and progressive leadership, sensitive to and aware of the fact that both problem and solution is the worker on the line, who simply needs to know, understand and be trained in the job performed.

Life in this country is a business of individual elective. The environmental occupational protection director who can effectively translate that into a safe and healthful workplace and into safe and healthful work practices is at a premium today and will be more so as time passes.

The Act, essential as it is, is only a mechanism. Environmental occupational protection is a people problem, is people oriented and people produced and solved.

CHAPTER THIRTEEN
Safety Inspection Guide

Safety inspection today unfortunately has only one connotation—the arrival of the CSHO, the man from OSHA, who is going to make things difficult. This is indeed unfortunate because a safety inspection as suggested here was here long before the Act came into effect. It has been a profitable and valuable tool for industry employing it, and with or without an Act it is in some ways the principal key to a successful environmental occupational protection program.

If a general check were made regularly—checking specifics against the Standards to make certain of compliance—the impending visit of a CSHO would not be cause for alarm but rather an opportunity to check all areas with the CSHO with a minimum or absence of alleged violations and suggested fines. When the safety inspection guide is used in checking your plant, it is a good idea to make a list of those things that need to be done. Then waste no time in getting them done. One Safety Director made an inspection of one of his company's facilities, noting 83 violations of good safe practice. When the plant was visited later by a CSHO, there were three alleged violations, and one very minor fine was assessed.

HOW TO MAKE A SAFETY INSPECTION

DETECTING UNSAFE PRACTICES, CONDITIONS AND HAZARDS

To be effective, safety and fire protection activities have to be a continuing day-to-day part of supervision and not something that is merely thought of once a month at the time of safety meetings or a safety and fire protection inspection. Supervisors must be constantly alert to the physical conditions of their area in order to detect and correct unsafe conditions and fire hazards. When going through their area, they should look about them in order to observe the working habits and practices of their employees. Safe working habits are developed in employees when supervisors continuously demonstrate their interest by maintaining a firm and consistent approach and by taking immediate corrective action whenever an unsafe practice is observed. In this manner, employees soon realize that they are expected to work safely at all times and will thus develop good working habits. Some of the main points are itemized below:

1. The basic responsibility for maintaining a safe environment rests with the supervisor of the area. Periodic inspections by supervision are, therefore, essential. It is desirable that a member of supervision from the area being inspected accompany any outside inspector to explain applicable area operations rules, and to exercise close surveillance in detecting unsafe practices and conditions which have not been recognized during day to day activities.

2. Outside inspectors should report to area supervisors and explain in detail what violations were found, if area supervisors did not accompany them during the inspection.

3. An inspector should remember that his conduct must be above reproach while inspecting an area. To do this he must be familiar with and obey all area safety rules, such as the wearing of respirators, hard hats, eye protection, special shoes, long sleeves, etc. Nothing makes so bad an impression as a safety inspector violating area rules.

4. When making a report say the same things to all concerned. For example, do not tell an area supervisor that his area is good and write a report to his boss about how the area is falling apart. Tell the same story to all levels of supervision.

5. When reporting unsafe practices and conditions, it is more important to report the cause than the item itself. Unless the cause is corrected the item will continue to appear on all future inspections.

6. Follow-up. An inspection that is not followed up to check on results is only half done. Make sure that you follow up on the action taken by area supervision. Promptness and sincerity of purpose should be displayed in the course of correcting unsafe conditions and situations.

7. Another point of caution is that supervision cannot look the other

way or condone relatively minor unsafe acts to avoid an unpleasant situation. Such action is detrimental to the entire safety program and will undermine the morale of employees.

MAIN POINTS TO LOOK FOR

Observe unsafe practices and conditions and make corrective action through line supervision. However, if an unsafe condition or practice could result in an injury at that particular time, the job should be stopped immediately and corrective action taken. An unsafe practice is defined as the breaking of any safety or operating rule, or any other act performed by an individual or individuals in which injury could result.

A few of the common points to be observed are itemized below:

UNSAFE CONDITIONS
1. missing guards on machinery, valves, flanges, etc.
2. tripping and slipping hazards
3. cluttered workspace
4. broken glass
5. cutting and pinching hazards
6. improper lock-out procedure
7. inspection on ladders delinquent
8. inspection on electric cords delinquent
9. inspection on steam hoses delinquent
10. improper use of safety rope
11. compressed gas cylinders not anchored, labeled or stored correctly
12. unguarded electric transmission lines in vicinity of men working
13. leaking process and service lines
14. safety chains
15. missing vapor proof globes on lights
16. electric control switches not identified
17. safety equipment in poor condition
18. uninsulated heat sources (steam lines, heat exchangers, etc.)
19. dusts, fumes, gases and vapors
20. lack of proper warning signs where needed

UNSAFE PRACTICES
1. climbing on tank tops, pipe lines, etc. without proper safety equipment
2. failure to wear proper personal protective equipment such as eye protection, hard hats, long sleeves, etc.

3. unauthorized smoking
4. working from ladders not tied off or held
5. working without proper and applicable permits
6. working on jobs without first having locked-out correctly
7. using steam hoses with pressure above 25 p.s.i. without proper authorization
8. failure to observe plant traffic regulations
9. poor pedestrian practices
10. working with improper tools

REFERENCE SECTION
Specific measurements referred to in this section are to be used for new installations. Although these may be desirable for existing installations, it must be pointed out that these measurements represent ideal conditions and judgment should be exercised as to whether or not existing facilities should be altered. Existing locations not meeting these requirements should be properly marked to identify any existing hazard. This section is primarily intended for reference.

BUILDINGS AND GROUNDS

RAMPS
1. adequate width and evenness for safe operation
2. not too steep for safe operation and never over 20 degrees unless auxiliary means for lowering
3. free of slipping and tripping hazards
4. surfaced with suitable nonslip material whenever danger of slipping is present
5. ramps less than 4 feet above the ground shall not require handrails

OVERHEAD MINIMUM CLEARANCES
1. platforms, stairs, and other regular routes of foot travel: 7' 0"
2. roadways: 15' 0"
3. broad-gauge tracks: 22' 0"

LATERAL MINIMUM CLEARANCES
1. regular routes of foot travel: 36"
2. passage between machines: 24"
3. safety exits and doorways: 28"
4. gangplanks and runways: 30"
5. runways for two-wheel hand trucks (two-way traffic): 60"
6. broad-gauge tracks: 8' 0" from center of track

WINDOWS
1. does pivot sash create bumping hazard?
2. does cracked or broken glass create hazard?
3. is sash in poor repair or in need of paint?
4. do latches work? are safety chains in place?
5. check condition of sash cords, chains or tubular balances (for fire windows, see Fire Protection Equipment)

VENTILATION
1. are ventilated hoods regularly inspected for air velocity?

DOORS
1. height of doors shall be 7' 0" or taller. Interior doors with light traffic and no overhead obstructions may be 6' 8"
2. double swinging doors have transparent panel
3. should not swing toward stairs unless adequate platform is provided
4. open outward where practical

DRAINS AND DITCHES
1. are they kept clear of obstructions?
2. do they have fume and vapor traps where needed?
3. are they located for maximum drainage?
4. are they properly covered to prevent tripping?
5. are they properly guarded?

CAR SPOTS
1. ease of operation
2. static ground wires maintained
3. proper storage of measuring rods, sample bottles. Protectoseal dome covers, gaskets, flanges, car chocks, signs, etc.
4. adequate lighting for night work
5. safety shower for corrosive materials
6. indicating lights for retractable platform working (if present)

EXITS
1. buildings two stories or more—a minimum of two exits
2. exits must never be blocked
3. emergency exit doors—use only safety latches
4. safety chute: good repair, no obstructions, not for material slide
5. lights provided over each exit; and on at night if building is used
6. doors open outward

ELECTRICAL EQUIPMENT

1. fuses and wire of proper size (not over 15 amps on lighting circuits)
2. no missing conduit covers
3. loose or missing grounds
4. 3-wire or self-insulating cords on all portable devices
5. all devices approved for electrical classification of building (check electric clocks, telephones, desk lamps, motors, switches, etc.)
6. flashlights: only explosion-proof allowed for plant use, unless such are not necessary
7. proper identification on switches and controls

ILLUMINATION

1. adequate for type of work
2. clean globes free of cracks
3. proper gaskets under globe
4. use proper type and size of globe
5. burned-out lamps promptly replaced

STAIRS

1. risers 9" high maximum
2. tread width 10" minimum exclusive of 1" nosing
3. stairs carrying 50 or more persons at one time at least 44" wide, those carrying 10-50—36" wide, and those carrying less than 10 people—30"
4. landing width to be same as stair widths
5. railing 39" above outer edge of tread excluding nosing
6. stairs 4' or wider or space between side of stairs and wall: double railing. Handrails required on both sides of stairs 44" or wider
7. keep clear at all times

RAILINGS

1. not less than 30" above floor; midtail 21" above floor (4" toe-board where necessary) at all open sides and ends of platforms if vertical drop is 4' or more
2. required for lesser heights if conditions warrant, i.e., over moving machinery, open tanks, etc.

FLOORS

1. smooth for walking or trucking
2. adequate support for stored material
3. marked storage areas

4. clear of tripping and slipping hazards
5. ramps or steps over low obstructions
6. holes properly guarded

OUTSIDE WALKS
1. level and clear of obstructions
2. at least 3' wide
3. adequate drainage

ELEVATORS AND LIFTS
1. inspected once per month
2. pits kept clean and drained
3. door interlocks function
4. operated only by authorized personnel
5. load sign posted

HOISTS, CHAIN BLOCKS, WINCHES, ETC.
1. visually inspected quarterly and an annual teardown inspection; year of teardown stenciled on equipment
2. personnel not under loads
3. never overload—capacity marked on hoist
4. any evidence of damage to any part
5. adequate supporting steel

HEATING AND/OR AIR CONDITIONING
1. exposed steam lines insulated up to 6' 6" above floor level
2. steam pressure to radiators not to exceed 25 p.s.i.; to blowers 40 p.s.i.
3. all equipment in good condition

FILE CABINET AND DRAWERS
1. file cabinets anchored to prevent tilting (two or more may be bolted together)
2. drawer stops provided

PORTABLE ELECTRIC EQUIPMENT AND EXTENSION CORDS
1. inspected monthly and tagged

NONPORTABLE ELECTRIC EQUIPMENT
1. inspected annually and tagged, except on instruments included as part of the preventive maintenance program

BONDING
1. painted red in "odd" years and yellow in "even" years; bonded with nylon string

ELECTRICAL AND STATIC GROUNDING

1. on storage tanks
2. on tank car loading platforms
3. on transformer bank fences
4. on flammable liquid containers
5. on pipe lines entering hazardous areas or buildings
6. on tank trucks
7. on tank cars and railroad tracks
8. on electric motors
9. on steam or flammable liquid hoses
10. on explosives buildings
11. for lightning protection

SAFETY EQUIPMENT

SAFETY SHOWERS

1. test once per shift until water is clear, or mud is out
2. during freezing weather, make certain that the unlagged portion of the shower drains properly and that there is no ice formation on the floor or ground under the shower
3. on steam-traced safety showers, make sure first water that comes out is not hot
4. do not obstruct approach to shower
5. valve handle should pull toward person using shower and operate easily
6. green light should always be on, with switch properly marked to stay on
7. valve handle placed 3' above floor level and located where needed

STRETCHER BOXES

1. know location
2. check stretcher hinges
3. check box hinges and latch
4. check points where canvas is attached to wood frames

AIR MASKS

1. maintained
2. check for proper use and connections in field. Valves blocked open by man wearing air mask, prepared and tagged by qualified E.R.D. attendant

GAS MASKS

1. stored in labeled mask box; latch and hinges on box work easily; no other materials stored in box

2. sealed in plastic bag (does not apply to Chemox or Scott)
3. inspected monthly
4. box properly located for emergency use
5. return used masks for service
6. canister gas masks acceptable only for protection against nuisance concentrations of toxic materials or for use as a high grade respirator

LIFE BELTS AND ROPES
1. tested every six months and marked
2. stored neatly in properly labeled box
3. no other materials stored in box
4. rope or belt should have no visual evidence of corrosion or contamination

ACID SUITS
1. stored properly
2. kept clean
3. undamaged
4. clear lens for hood

GOGGLE CLEANING STATION
1. adequate supply of cleaning tissues
2. receptacle for disposal of tissue
3. evidence that it is being used

SAFETY RULES
1. properly posted and up to date
2. cover new processes
3. reviewed periodically
4. covered with all new or transferred employees

BULLETIN BOARD
1. neat display
2. no obsolete (outdated) material or notices
3. good location

SAFETY SIGNS
1. right signs for job
2. signs in good condition

SAFETY ROPE
1. used to temporarily rope off unsafe conditions
2. properly tagged
3. used in proper locations
4. removed promptly after unsafe condition has been eliminated

EYE WASH BOTTLES
1. full and in good condition
2. located near applicable operations

FIRE PROTECTION EQUIPMENT

FIRE DOORS
1. not obstructed in any way
2. closes completely
3. counterweight is guarded
4. door is in good condition
5. door is printed red
6. rollers, track and chain are properly lubricated

FIRE ALARM BOXES
1. know location
2. unobstructed
3. red light always on
4. know how to operate
5. know how to report a fire

FIRE HYDRANT AND HOSE STATIONS AND HOUSES
1. know locations of all boxes within area
2. is hose dry and clean
3. nozzles and wrenches O.K.
4. box in good repair
5. access not blocked

FIRE EXTINGUISHERS
1. unobstructed
2. proper type of extinguisher for potential fires
3. post on background marked with red paint on all extinguishers (office buildings excepted)
4. check hose for plugged nozzle tips
5. condition of hose, especially where it is connected to extinguisher
6. lift or look to see if it is full
7. check last inspection date (annually)
8. is location best—near exit and fire source
9. extinguisher should be numbered

SPRINKLER SYSTEM
1. does it give complete coverage (under tanks, platforms, roof peaks, main building supports, flammable drumming booth, dryers).
2. nothing stored within 18" of sprinkler heads
3. nothing hung from sprinkler pipes

4. heads not corroded or painted over
5. lines identified by good paint job (red in operating building)
6. post indicator valve open
7. not to be used for electrical ground

MATERIAL HANDLING

STORAGE AND PILING
1. neat and orderly
2. not too high
3. accessible
4. personnel wearing proper protective equipment
5. proper identification
6. safe mechanical devices
7. loads not too bulky or heavy for employees or mechanical equipment
8. operators of mechanical equipment properly trained

PRECAUTIONS TAKEN FOR FOLLOWING
1. heavy
2. long
3. rough, sharp
4. slippery
5. flammable
6. hot
7. cold
8. fragile
9. poisonous
10. corrosive

OPERATING EQUIPMENT

PIPE LINES
1. flange and valve guards where needed
2. properly hung
3. remove if obsolete
4. safety valves where required

GAS CYLINDERS
1. transporting (damaged cap threads? regulators off? protective cap in place?)
2. storage (upright with chain)
3. supporting
4. manifolding (supplied by vendor, not home made; don't force odd threads)
5. identification (properly labeled; tear off tag properly used)

GUARDS
1. does it adequately cover moving machinery?
2. is it a permanent guard?
3. check condition carefully

GRINDING WHEELS
1. check for Perks washers (flanges); (cover at least 50% of wheel)
2. check position of tool rest (not to exceed 1/8 inch from wheel)
3. check guards around wheel

LAYOUT
1. adequate room for moving materials
2. adequate passageways and exits

TOOLS
1. inspected every three months
2. properly stored
3. in good condition
4. right tool for job

MAINTENANCE
1. inspect overall physical condition, paint, etc. of building and equipment
2. housekeeping

VENTS AND FLAME ARRESTORS
1. vessels containing flammable materials properly protected
2. each unit inspected quarterly

CONTROLS
1. properly identified

TEMPORARY EQUIPMENT
1. safely installed
2. adequate for job
3. not to be used for other purposes
4. should be replaced by permanent installation

LADDERS
1. portable ladders inspected semi-annually
2. fixed steel ladders inspected annually and marked
3. tie rope
4. check for damage
5. proper feet (Dayton A-500 ladder feet or spikes)
6. proper storage

STEAM HOSES
1. identified by yellow painted section on both ends
2. inspected quarterly by pipe shop and tagged
3. equipped with Boss coupling

AIR HOSES
1. inspected quarterly by pipe shop and tagged

PRESSURE RELIEF VALVE AND RUPTURE DISCS
1. applicable installations properly sized
2. inspected annually (month and year on lead seal)

UNFIRED PRESSURE VESSELS
1. all vessels qualifying as unfired pressure vessels must be hydro-statically tested at least once every five years

SCAFFOLDS
1. scaffold planks not to be used for any other purpose; inspected annually and marked with year inspected
2. scaffolds built correctly and inspected each day by those people using them

HOUSEKEEPING
1. neat and orderly arrangement of process material and portable equipment
2. floors and equipment clean
3. no foreign materials
4. a place for everything and everything in its place
5. adequate trash disposal facilities being used
6. facilities for disposal of dangerous materials such as:
   a. acids or other irritating chemicals
   b. explosives
   c. oxidizing agents
   d. glass or other sharp objects
   e. other applicable items not listed above

SANITATION AND HEALTH

TOILETS AND URINALS
1. keep clean
2. adequate supply of tissue
3. adequate ventilation

WASHING AND BATHING FACILITIES
1. hands and face washed before lunch when working with toxic materials

2. shower after exposure to contamination and/or at end of work shift
3. adequate hot water, basins, and number of showers to take care of rush periods
4. enough soap, other cleansers, paper towels
5. facilities kept clean
6. water temperature at faucet not over 145°F.

DRINKING WATER
1. only from drinking water lines
2. no connections between drinking water and any other lines
3. convenient locations
4. kept cool
5. fountains clean

LOCKERS
1. adequate storage space
2. adequate ventilation
3. periodic inspections
4. properly anchored lockers
5. benches provided

EATING
1. where permitted
2. a convenient, ventilated lunch room separated from operating area
3. kept clean
4. proper trash disposal facilities

PERSONNEL

CLOTHING
1. free of contaminants
2. no frayed edges to trip or catch in equipment
3. flame retardant where required
4. adequate coverage: sleeves buttoned at wrist, one button open at neck in area required
5. hat or cap
6. safety shoes in good condition

PERSONAL PROTECTIVE EQUIPMENT
1. safety glasses, properly fitted
2. gloves for type of work
3. hard hats required

4. availability and use of goggles, face masks, safety belts, air line respirators, acid suits, etc. where needed

UNSAFE PRACTICES

1. observe unsafe practices and conditions and make corrective action through line supervision. However, if an unsafe condition or practice could result in an injury at that particular time, the job should be stopped immediately and corrective action taken

SAFETY MEETINGS

1. held at regular intervals (at least monthly)
2. held on time
3. planned
4. effective
5. cover entire group

JOB TRAINING

1. new men should be well instructed in their job procedures
2. older employees should be retrained for new job
3. job procedures should be up-to-date and readily available

CHAPTER FOURTEEN
National Personnel Administrating
The Occupational Safety and Health
Act of 1970

DEPARTMENT OF LABOR

Most offices of the Department of Labor are located in the Main Labor Building at Fourteenth Street and Constitution Avenue, N.W., Washington, D.C. 20210, and offices listed in this directory, unless otherwise noted, are in that building. The area code for Washington is 202, and the general telephone number for offices in the Main Labor Building is 961-2001, unless otherwise designated below.

Secretary of Labor .... James D. Hodgson
Assistant Secretary of Labor for
Occupational Safety and Health .... George C. Guenther
Deputy Assistant Secretary for
Occupational Safety and Health .... Marl Chain Robbins

OCCUPATIONAL SAFETY AND HEALTH ADMINISTRATION REGIONAL, AREA AND DISTRICT OFFICES; NAMES OF COORDINATING PERSONNEL

REGION I—Boston
(Connecticut, Maine, Massachusetts, New Hampshire, Rhode Island, Vermont)
Regional Administrator: Donald A. Mackenzie, U. S. Department

of Labor, Occupational Safety & Health Administration, John F. Kennedy Federal Building, Government Center—308 E. Boston, Massachusetts 02203. FTS & Comm. Telephone: 617-223-6712/3 and 4538/9.

AREA OFFICES

Richard Amirault, Area Director, U. S. Department of Labor, Occupational Safety & Health Administration, Federal Building—Room 425, 55 Pleasant St., Concord, New Hampshire 03301. FTS Telephone: 603-224-7725. Comm.: 603-224-1995/6.[1]

John V. Fiatarone, Area Director, U. S. Department of Labor, Occupational Safety & Health Administration, Custom House Building, State St., Boston, Massachusetts 02109. FTS & Comm. Telephone: 617-223-4511/2.

Harold Smith, Area Director, U. S. Department of Labor, Occupational Safety & Health Administration, Federal Building—Room 617, 450 Main St., Hartford, Connecticut 06103. FTS & Comm. Telephone: 203-244-2294.

District Office

Steven J. Simms, District Supervisor, U. S. Department of Labor, Occupational Safety & Health Administration, Federal Bldg., U. S. Court House, Room 503-A, Providence, Rhode Island 02903. FTS & Comm. Telephone: 401-528-4466.

REGION II—New York
(New Jersey, New York, Puerto Rico, Virgin Islands)

Alfred Barden, Regional Administrator, U. S. Department of Labor, Occupational Safety & Health Administration, 1515 Broadway (1 Astor Plaza), Room 3445, New York, New York 10036. FTS & Comm. Telephone: 212-971-5941/2.

AREA OFFICES

Nicholas A. DiArchangel, Area Director, U. S. Department of Labor, Occupational Safety & Health Administration, 90 Church St., Room 1405, New York, New York 10007. FTS & Comm. Telephone: 212-971-9840/1/2.

William J. Druland, Area Director, U. S. Department of Labor, Occupational Safety & Health Administration, Room 635, Federal Office Building, 970 Broad St., Newark, N. J. 07102. FTS & Comm. Telephone: 201-645-5930/1/2.

[1]FTS phone numbers are used by federal government employees, and commercial phone numbers are used by the general public. When there is direct dialing, as for the Boston Regional Office, one number is used for both purposes. In other cases, as for the Concord Area Office, separate numbers are used.

James H. Epps, Area Director, U. S. Department of Labor, Occupational Safety and Health Administration, 370 Old Country Road, Garden City, New York 11530. FTS & Comm. Telephone: 212-971-5754/5.

Louis Jacob, Area Director, U. S. Department of Labor, Occupational Safety & Health Administration, Condominium San Alberto Bldg., 605 Condado Ave., Room 328, Santurce, Puerto Rico 00907. FTS & Comm. Telephone: 809-724-1059.

Chester Whitehead, U. S. Department of Labor, Occupational Safety & Health Administration, Room 203, Midtown Plaza, 700 East Water Street, Syracuse, N. Y. 13210. FTS & Comm. Telephone: 315-473-2700/1.

REGION III—Philadelphia
(Delaware, District of Columbia, Maryland,
Pennsylvania, Virginia, West Virginia)

David H. Rhone, Regional Administrator, U. S. Department of Labor, Occupational Safety & Health Administration, Penn Square Bldg.—Room 623, 1317 Filbert St., Philadelphia, Pennsylvania 19107. FTS & Comm. Telephone: 215-597-4102/3/4.

AREA OFFICES

Byron R. Chadwick, Area Director, U. S. Department of Labor, Occupational Safety & Health Administration, 3661 Virginia Beach Blvd., Stanwick Bldg., Rm. 111, Norfolk, Virginia 23502. FTS & Comm. Telephone: 703-441-6381/2.

Maurice R. Daly, Area Director, U. S. Department of Labor, Occupational Safety & Health Administration, Federal Bldg.—Room 1110A, 31 Hopkins Plaza, Charles Center, Baltimore, Maryland 21201. FTS & Comm. Telephone: 301-962-2840.

Lapsley C. Ewing, Area Director, U. S. Department of Labor, Occupational Safety & Health Administration, Room 8018—Federal Bldg., P.O. Box 10186, 400 North 8th St., Richmond, Virginia 23240. FTS & Comm. Telephone: 703-782-2241/2.

Harry G. Lacey, Area Director, U. S. Department of Labor, Occupational Safety & Health Administration, Room 445D—Federal Bldg., 1000 Liberty Ave., Pittsburgh, Pennsylvania 15222. FTS & Comm. Telephone: 412-644-2905/6.

Harry Sachkar, Area Director, U. S. Department of Labor, Occupational Safety & Health Administration, 1317 Filbert St.—Suite 1010, Philadelphia, Pennsylvania 19107. FTS & Comm. Telephone: 215-597-4955.

REGION IV—Atlanta
(Alabama, Florida, Georgia, Kentucky, Mississippi,
North Carolina, South Carolina, Tennessee)
Basil A. Needham, Jr., Regional Administrator, U. S. Department of Labor, Occupational Safety & Health Administration, 1375 Peachtree St., N.E.—Suite 587, Atlanta, Georgia 30309. FTS & Comm. Telephone: 404-526-3573/4 or 3629/3620 or 5797/8.

AREA OFFICES

Bernard E. Addy, Area Director, U. S. Department of Labor, Occupational Safety & Health Administration, Enterprise Bldg.— Suite 201, 6605 Abercorn Expy., Savannah, Georgia 31405. FTS Telephone: 912-232-4393; Comm.: 912-354-0733.

James E. Blount, Area Director, U. S. Department of Labor, Occupational Safety & Health Administration, Room 204, Bridge Bldg., 3200 E. Oakland Park Blvd., Fort Lauderdale, Florida 33308. FTS Telephone: 305-350-7331; Comm.: 305-525-0611x331.

Joseph L. Camp, Area Director, U. S. Department of Labor, Occupational Safety & Health Administration, Todd Mall, 2047 Canyon Rd., Birmingham, Alabama 35216. FTS Telephone: 205-325-6081; Comm.: 205-822-7100.

Frank P. Flanagan, Area Director, U. S. Department of Labor, Occupational Safety & Health Administration, Room 561—600 Federal Pl., Louisville, Kentucky 40202. FTS & Comm. Telephone: 502-582-6111/12.

William W. Gordon, Area Director, U. S. Department of Labor, Occupational Safety & Health Administration, U. S. Federal Office Bldg., 400 West Bay St., Box 35063, Jacksonville, Florida 32202. FTS & Comm. Telephone: 904-791-2895.

Quentin F. Haskins, Area Director, U. S. Department of Labor, Occupational Safety & Health Administration, 1361 East Morehead St., Charlotte, North Carolina 28204. FTS Telephone: 704-372-7495; Comm.: 704-372-0711x495.

Eugene E. Light, Area Director, U. S. Department of Labor, Occupational Safety & Health Administration, 1600 Hayes St.— Suite 302, Nashville, Tennessee 37203. FTS & Comm. Telephone: 615-749-5313.

William F. Moerlins, Area Director, U. S. Department of Labor, Occupational Safety & Health Administration, 1371 Peachtree St., N.E.—Rm. 723, Atlanta, Georgia 30309. FTS & Comm. Telephone: 404-526-5806/7 or 5883/4.

Harold J. Monegue, Area Director, U. S. Department of Labor, Occupational Safety & Health Administration, Commerce Bldg.—

Room 801, 118 North Royal St., Mobile, Alabama 36602. FTS Telephone: 205-433-3482; Comm.: 205-433-3581x482.

REGION V—Chicago
(Illinois, Indiana, Michigan, Minnesota, Ohio, Wisconsin)
Edward E. Estkowski, Regional Administrator, U. S. Department of Labor, Occupational Safety & Health Administration, 300 South Wacker Drive—Room 1201, Chicago, Illinois 60606. FTS & Comm. Telephone: 312-353-4716/17.

AREA OFFICES
Kenneth Bowman, Area Director, U. S. Department of Labor, Occupational Safety & Health Administration, 847 Federal Office Bldg., 1240 East Ninth St., Cleveland, Ohio 44199. FTS & Comm. Telephone: 216-522-3818.

Glenn Butler, Area Director, U. S. Department of Labor, Occupational Safety & Health Administration, Room 734 Federal Office Bldg., 234 N. Summit St., Toledo, Ohio 43604. FTS & Comm. Telephone: 419-259-7542.

Vernon Fern, Area Director, U. S. Department of Labor, Occupational Safety & Health Administration, 110 South Fourth St.— Room 437, Minneapolis, Minnesota 55401. FTS & Comm. Telephone: 612-725-2571.

William Fucheon, Area Director, U. S. Department of Labor, Occupational Safety & Health Administration, 300 South Wacker Drive—Room 1200, Chicago, Illinois 60606. FTS & Comm. Telephone: 312-353-1390.

Robert B. Hanna, Area Director, U. S. Department of Labor, Occupational Safety & Health Administration, Clark Bldg., Room 400, 633 W. Wisconsin Ave., Milwaukee, Wisconsin 53203. FTS & Comm. Telephone: 414-224-3315/6.

J. Fred Keppler, Area Director, U. S. Department of Labor, Occupational Safety & Health Administration, U. S. Post Office and Courthouse, 46 East Ohio St.—Room 423, Indianapolis, Indiana 46204. FTS & Comm. Telephone: 317-633-7384.

Earl J. Krotzer, Area Director, U. S. Department of Labor, Occupational Safety & Health Administration, Michigan Theatre Bldg. —Rm. 626, 220 Bagley Ave., Detroit, Michigan 48226. FTS & Comm. Telephone: 313-226-6720.

Ronald McCann, Area Director, U. S. Department of Labor, Occupational Safety & Health Administration, Room 5522 Federal Office Bldg., 550 Main St., Cincinnati, Ohio 45202. FTS & Comm. Telephone: 513-684-2355.

Peter Schmitt, Area Director, U. S. Department of Labor, Occupational Safety & Health Administration, Room 224—Bryson Bldg., 700 Bryden Rd., Columbus, Ohio 43215. FTS & Comm. Telephone: 614-468-5582.

REGION VI—Dallas
(Arkansas, Louisiana, New Mexico, Oklahoma, Texas)
John K. Barto, Regional Administrator, U. S. Department of Labor, Occupational Safety & Health Administration, 7th Floor—Texaco Bldg., 1512 Commerce St., Dallas, Texas 75201. FTS & Comm. Telephone: 214-749-2477/8/9 or 2567.

AREA OFFICES
Charles J. Adams, Area Director, U. S. Department of Labor, Occupational Safety & Health Administration, Room 6B1—Federal Bldg., 1100 Commerce St., Dallas, Texas 75202. FTS & Comm. Telephone: 214-749-1786/7/8.

Thomas T. Curry, Area Director, U. S. Department of Labor, Occupational Safety & Health Administration, 307 Central National Bank Bldg., Houston, Texas 77002. FTS & Comm. Telephone: 713-226-5431.

James T. Knorpp, Area Director, U. S. Department of Labor, Occupational Safety & Health Administration, Room 512, Petroleum Bldg., 420 South Boulder, Tulsa, Oklahoma 74103. FTS Telephone: 918-584-7676; Comm.: 918-584-7151x7676.

John K. Parsons, Area Director, U. S. Department of Labor, Occupational Safety & Health Administration, 546 Cardondelet St., 4th Floor, New Orleans, Louisiana 70130. FTS & Comm. Telephone: 504-527-2451/2 or 6166/7.

Robert B. Simmons, Area Director, U. S. Department of Labor, Occupational Safety & Health Administration, Room 421—Federal Bldg., 1205 Texas Ave., Lubbock, Texas 79401. FTS Telephone: 806-747-3681; Comm.: 806-747-3711x3681.

District Office
Burtrand C. Lindquist, District Supervisor, U. S. Department of Labor, Occupational Safety & Health Administration, U. S. Customs House Bldg.—Room 325, Galveston, Texas 77550. FTS & Comm. Telephone: 713-763-1472/4.

REGION VII—Kansas City, Missouri
(Iowa, Kansas, Missouri, Nebraska)
Joseph A. Reidinger, Regional Administrator, U. S. Department of Labor, Occupational Safety & Health Administration, Room 300,

Waltower Bldg., 823 Walnut St., Kansas City, Missouri 64106. FTS & Comm. Telephone: 816-374-5249/5240.

AREA OFFICES

Robert J. Borchardt, Area Director, U. S. Department of Labor, Occupational Safety & Health Administration, 1627 Main St.—Room 1100, Kansas City, Missouri 64108. FTS & Comm. Telephone: 816-374-2756.

Angelo F. Castranova, Area Director, U. S. Department of Labor, Occupational Safety & Health Administration, Federal Bldg.— 210 N. 12th St., Room 533, St. Louis, Missouri 63103. FTS & Comm. Telephone: 314-622-5061/2.

Warren P. Wright, Area Director, U. S. Department of Labor, Occupational Safety & Health Administration, City National Bank Bldg.—Room 630, Harney and 16th Streets, Omaha, Nebraska 68102. FTS & Comm. Telephone: 402-221-3276/7.

REGION VIII—Denver

(Colorado, Montana, North Dakota, South Dakota, Utah, Wyoming)

Howard J. Schulte, Regional Administrator, U. S. Department of Labor, Occupational Safety & Health Administration, Federal Bldg. —Room 15010, P.O. Box 3588, 1961 Stout St., Denver, Colorado 80202. FTS & Comm. Telephone: 303-837-3883.

AREA OFFICES

Charles F. Hines, Area Director, U. S. Department of Labor, Occupational Safety & Health Administration, Suite 309—Executive Bldg., 455 East 4th South, Salt Lake City, Utah 84111. FTS & Comm. Telephone: 301-524-5080.

Vernon A. Strahm, Area Director, U. S. Department of Labor, Occupational Safety & Health Administration, Suite 525, Petroleum Bldg., 2812 1st Ave. N., Billings, Montana 59101. FTS Telephone: 406-245-6640/6649; Comm.: 406-245-6711x6640 or 6649.

Jerome J. Williams, Area Director, U. S. Department of Labor, Occupational Safety & Health Administration, Squire Plaza Bldg., 8527 W. Colfax Ave., Lakewood, Colorado 80215. FTS & Comm. Telephone 303-827-3883.

REGION IX—San Francisco

(Arizona, California, Hawaii, Nevada, Guam, American Samoa, Trust Territory of the Pacific Islands)

Gabriel Gillotti, Acting Administrator, U. S. Department of Labor, Occupational Safety & Health Administration, 9470 Federal Bldg., 450 Golden Gate Ave., Box 36017, San Francisco, California 94102. FTS & Comm. Telephone: 415-556-0584 or 4427.

AREA OFFICES

Lawrence E. Gromachey, Area Director, U. S. Department of Labor, Occupational Safety & Health Administration, Suite 910— Amerco Towers, 2721 North Central Ave., Phoenix, Arizona 85004. FTS & Comm. Telephone: 602-261-4857/8.

Paul F. Haygood, Area Director, U. S. Department of Labor, Occupational Safety & Health Administration, 333 Queen St., Suite 505, Honolulu, Hawaii 96813. FTS & Comm. Telephone: 808-546-3157/8.

Anthony Mignano, Area Director, U. S. Department of Labor, Occupational Safety & Health Administration, Hartwell Bldg.— Room 514, 19 Pine Ave., Long Beach, California 90802. FTS Telephone: 213-831-9281, then ask Long Beach FTS operator for 432-3434. Comm.: 213-432-3434.

Donald T. Pickford, Area Director, U. S. Department of Labor, Occupational Safety & Health Administration, 100 McAllister St.— Room 1706, San Francisco, California 94102. FTS & Comm. Telephone: 415-556-0536.

REGION X—Seattle
(Alaska, Idaho, Oregon, Washington)

James W. Lake, Regional Administrator, U. S. Department of Labor, Occupational Safety & Health Administration, 506 Second Ave., 1808 Smith Tower Bldg., Seattle, Washington 98104. FTS & Comm. Telephone: 206-442-5930.

AREA OFFICES

Richard L. Beeston, U. S. Department of Labor, Occupational Tower Bldg., Seattle, Washington 98104. FTS & Comm. Telephone: Safety & Health Administration, 506 Second Ave., 1906 Smith 206-442-7520/7527.

Eugene Harrower, U. S. Department of Labor, Occupational Safety & Health Administration, Room 526—Pittock Block, 921 S.W. Washington St., Portland, Oregon 97205. FTS & Comm. Telephone: 503-221-2251.

Darrell Miller, U. S. Department of Labor, Occupational Safety & Health Administration, 610 C Street, Willholth Bldg., Room 214, Anchorage, Alaska 99501.

OCCUPATIONAL SAFETY AND HEALTH REVIEW COMMISSION
1825 K Street, N.W., Washington, D.C.
Telephone: 202-382-6214

Members
   Robert D. Moran, Chairman. Term expires April 28, 1977.
      Chief Legal Counsel: Edwin C. Satter III
   James F. Van Namee. Term expires April 28, 1975.
      Chief Legal Counsel: W. Scott Railton
   Alan F. Burch. Term expires April 28, 1973.
      Chief Legal Counsel: Timothy F. Cleary

Key Personnel
   Acting Executive Director: Donald F. White
   Director of Judicial Administration: Patrick J. Creamer
   Acting Executive Secretary: Allen H. Sachsel
   General Counsel: Donald F. White
   Director of Administration: Richard H. L'Heureux
   Director of Information and Publications: Linda P. Dodd

Judges
   Herbert E. Bates, Washington, D.C.
   Paul L. Brady, Atlanta, Georgia
   William E. Brennan, Washington, D.C.
   Robert N. Burchmore, Los Angeles, California
   James D. Burroughs, Atlanta, Georgia
   John A. Carlson, Denver, Colorado
   John C. Castelli, Dallas, Texas
   Joseph L. Chalk, Washington, D.C.
   Charles K. Chaplin, Washington, D.C.
   Joseph Chodes, New York, New York
   James Anthony Cronin, Los Angeles, California
   I. Marker Dern, Atlanta, Georgia
   Jerome C. Ditore, New York, New York
   Paul E. Dixon, St. Louis, Missouri
   Thomas J. Donegan, Seattle, Washington
   Donald K. Duvall, Washington, D.C.
   Abraham M. Gold, Washington, D.C.
   Sidney J. Goldstein, Chicago, Illinois
   David Howard Harris, Washington, D.C.
   Harold A. Kennedy, Los Angeles, California
   John J. Larkin, Atlanta, Georgia
   Henry F. Martin, Dallas, Texas
   Jerry W. Mitchell, Seattle, Washington
   Leon J. Moran, Washington, D.C.
   John J. Morris, Denver, Colorado
   James P. O'Connell, New York, New York
   David G. Oringer, Atlanta, Georgia
   Henry K. Osterman, Washington, D.C.
   John S. Patton, Atlanta, Georgia
   Vernon G. Riehl, St. Louis, Missouri
   William J. Risteau, Los Angeles, California
   Louis J. Rubin, Chicago, Illinois
   Erwin D. Stuller, Los Angeles, California
   Garl Watkins, Seattle, Washington
   Robert P. Weil, Chicago, Illinois
   Alan M. Weinman, St. Louis, Missouri
   Ernest C. Winfrey, Dallas, Texas
   Henry C. Winters, Seattle, Washington

Benjamin D. Worcester, Washington, D.C.

David J. Knight, Silver Spring, Maryland

Judges' Offices (tentative locations)

Washington, D.C., 1825 K Street, N.W.—Judges will cover cases from OSHA Regions 1 and 3.

New York, New York, 1515 Broadway, Room 3210—Judges will cover cases from OSHA Region 2.

Atlanta, Georgia, 1365 Peachtree Street, Room 400—Judges will cover cases from OSHA Region 4.

Chicago, Illinois, 536 South Clark St., Room 1058—Judges will cover cases from OSHA Region 5.

Dallas, Texas, 1114 Commerce St., Room 1206—Judges will cover cases from OSHA Region 6.

St. Louis, Missouri, U. S. Court & Customs House Building, 1114 Market Street, Room 606—Judges will cover cases from OSHA Region 7.

Denver, Colorado, Main Post Office, 1823 Stout St., Room 296—Judges will cover cases from OSHA Region 8.

Los Angeles, California, 312 North Spring Street, Room 1009—Judges will cover cases from OSHA Region 9.

Seattle, Washington, 4144 A Federal Office Bldg., 909 1st Ave.—Judges will cover cases from OSHA Region 10.

BUREAU OF LABOR STATISTICS REGIONAL OFFICES AND NAMES OF REGIONAL DIRECTORS

REGION I

(Connecticut, Maine, Massachusetts, New Hampshire, Rhode Island, Vermont)

Regional Director: Wendell D. Macdonald, Bureau of Labor Statistics, 1603-A Federal Office Building, Boston, Massachusetts 02203. Telephone: 617-223-4541.

REGION II

(New Jersey, New York, Puerto Rico, Virgin Islands)

Regional Director: Herbert Bienstock, Bureau of Labor Statistics, 341 Ninth Avenue, New York, New York 10001. Telephone: 212-971-5915.

REGION III

(Delaware, District of Columbia, Maryland, Pennsylvania, Virginia, West Virginia)

Regional Director: Frederick W. Mueller, Bureau of Labor Statistics, Penn Square Building, Room 406, 1317 Filbert Street, Philadelphia, Pennsylvania 19107. Telephone: 215-597-7510.

REGION IV

(Alabama, Florida, Georgia, Kentucky, Mississippi, North Carolina, South Carolina, Tennessee)

Regional Director: Brunswick A. Bagdon, Bureau of Labor Statistics, 1317 Peachtree Street N.E., Atlanta, Georgia 30309. Telephone: 404-526-3660.

REGION V

(Illinois, Indiana, Michigan, Minnesota, Ohio, Wisconsin)
Regional Director: William E. Rice, Bureau of Labor Statistics, 219 S. Dearborn Street, Chicago, Illinois 60604. Telephone: 312-353-7253.

REGION VI

(Arkansas, Louisiana, New Mexico, Oklahoma, Texas)
Regional Director: Jack F. Strickland, Bureau of Labor Statistics, 1100 Commerce Street, Room 6B7, Dallas, Texas 75202. Telephone: 214-749-1781.

REGIONS VII AND VIII

(VII—Iowa, Kansas, Missouri, Nebraska; VIII—Colorado, Montana, North Dakota, South Dakota, Utah, Wyoming)
Regional Director: Elliott A. Browar, Bureau of Labor Statistics, Federal Office Building, 911 Walnut Street, Kansas City, Missouri 64106. Telephone: 816-374-3685.

REGIONS IX AND X

(IX—Arizona, California, Hawaii, Nevada;
X—Alaska, Idaho, Oregon, Washington)
Regional Director: Charles A. Roumasset, Bureau of Labor Statistics, 450 Golden Gate Avenue, Box 36017, San Francisco, California 94102. Telephone: 415-556-8980.

NATIONAL INSTITUTE FOR OCCUPATIONAL SAFETY AND HEALTH

Headquarters: NIOSH, Health Services and Mental Health Administration, 5600 Fishers Lane, Rockville, Maryland 20852.

Cincinnati Laboratory: NIOSH, Health Services and Mental Health Administration, 1014 Broadway, Cincinnati, Ohio 45202.

Appalachian Laboratory: Appalachian Center for Occupational Safety and Health, NIOSH, P.O. Box 4292, Morgantown, West Virginia 26505.

Western Area Laboratory: Western Area Occupational Health Laboratory, NIOSH, 2738 South 20th East, Salt Lake City, Utah 84106. Mailing Address: P.O. Box 8137, Salt Lake City, Utah 84108.

Director: Dr. Marcus M. Key; A. C. Blackman, Assistant Director for Safety.

Regional Directors and Offices:

REGION I—Boston

(Connecticut, Maine, Massachusetts, New Hampshire,
Rhode Island, Vermont)
Regional Program Director, (Vacant), NIOSH, DHEW Region I, Government Center (JFK Fed. Bldg.), Boston, Massachusetts 02203.

REGION II—New York City
(New Jersey, New York, Puerto Rico, Virgin Islands)
Regional Program Director, (Vacant), NIOSH, DHEW Region II,
Federal Bldg., 26 Federal Plaza, New York, New York 10007.

REGION III—Philadelphia
(Delaware, District of Columbia, Maryland,
Pennsylvania, Virginia, West Virginia)
Regional Program Director, William Shoemaker, NIOSH, DHEW
Region III, 401 North Broad Street, Philadelphia, Pennsylvania
19108.

REGION IV—Atlanta
(Alabama, Florida, Georgia, Kentucky, Mississippi,
North Carolina, South Carolina, Tennessee)
Regional Program Director, Kenneth Kronoveter, NIOSH, DHEW
Region IV, 50 Seventh Street, N.E., Atlanta, Georgia 30323.

REGION V—Chicago
(Illinois, Indiana, Michigan, Minnesota, Ohio, Wisconsin)
Regional Program Director, Marshall Laneir, NIOSH, DHEW
Region V, 300 South Wacker Drive, Chicago, Illinois 60607.

REGION VI—Dallas
(Arkansas, Louisiana, New Mexico, Oklahoma, Texas)
Regional Program Director, George Pettigrew, NIOSH, DHEW
Region VI, 1100 Commerce Street, Room 8-C-53, Dallas, Texas
75202.

REGION VII—Kansas City, Missouri
(Iowa, Kansas, Missouri, Nebraska)
Regional Program Director, Ralph Bicknell, NIOSH, DHEW Re-
gion VII, 601 East 12th Street, Kansas City, Missouri 64106.

REGION VIII—Denver
(Colorado, Montana, North Dakota, South Dakota, Utah, Wyoming)
Regional Program Director, Stanley Reno, NIOSH, DHEW Region VIII, 19th and Stout Sts. (9017 Fed. Bldg.), Denver, Colorado
80202.

REGION IX—San Francisco
(Arizona, California, Hawaii, Nevada)
Regional Program Director, Douglas Johnson, NIOSH, DHEW
Region IX, 50 Fulton Street (254 FOB), San Francisco, California
94102.

REGION X—Seattle
(Alaska, Idaho, Oregon, Washington)

Regional Program Director, Walter E. Ruch, NIOSH, DHEW Region X, 1321 Second Avenue (Arcade Bldg.), Seattle, Washington 98101.

OCCUPATIONAL SAFETY AND HEALTH
PROGRAM ADMINISTRATORS

The following is a list of the persons and offices designated as being in charge of the occupational safety and health programs.

Alabama
Howard E. Hendrix, Director
Department of Labor
Montgomery, Alabama 36104

Alaska
Henry A. Benson
Commissioner
Department of Labor
Post Office Box 1149
Juneau, Alaska 99801
Jack Garrett, Director
Industrial Safety Division
Department of Labor
710 McKay Bldg.
338 Denali
Anchorage, Alaska 99501

American Samoa
Ben Schirmer, Administrator
Office of Workmen's Compensation
Pago Pago, American Samoa

Arizona
Robert Kley, Director
Industrial Commission of Arizona
Post Office Box 7575
Phoenix, Arizona 85011

Arkansas
Dale Cline
Commissioner
Department of Labor
Capitol Hill Building
Little Rock, Arkansas 72201

California
William C. Hern
Department of Industrial Relations
State Building Annex
Post Office Box 603
455 Golden Gate Avenue
San Francisco, California 94101

Colorado
James M. Shaffer
Executive Director
200 East Ninth Avenue
Denver, Colorado 80203

Connecticut
Franklin Foote, Commissioner
Connecticut Dept. of Health
79 Elm Street
Hartford, Connecticut 06115
Jack A. Fusari, Commissioner
Connecticut Dept. of Labor
200 Folly Brook Blvd.
Hartford, Connecticut 06115

Delaware
James M. Rosbrow, Secretary
Dept. of Labor and Industrial
  Relations
801 West Tenth Street
Wilmington, Delaware 19801

District of Columbia
Walter E. Washington, Mayor-
  Commissioner
The District of Columbia
Washington, D. C. 20004
Charles T. Green
Director of Industrial Safety
Minimum Wage and Safety
  Board
615 "I" Street N.W.
Washington, D.C. 20001

Florida
Stephen Slepin, Director
Department of Commerce
Caldwell Building
Tallahassee, Florida 32301

Georgia
Kirby J. Winters
Bureau of State Planning and
  Community Affairs
270 Washington St., S.W.
Atlanta, Georgia 30334

Guam
Department of Labor
Government of Guam
Post Office Box 884
Agana, Guam 96910

Hawaii
Robert K. Hasegawa
Director of Labor and Indus-
  trial Relations
825 Mililani Street
Honolulu, Hawaii 96813

Idaho
Will S. Defenbach, Chairman
Industrial Accident Board
Industrial Administration Bldg.
317 Main Street
Boise, Idaho 83702

Illinois
Barney J. Grabiec, Director
Department of Labor
160 North LaSalle Street
Chicago, Illinois 60601
Alexander White, Chairman
Illinois Industrial Commission
160 North LaSalle Street
Chicago, Illinois 60601

Indiana
William Lanam, Commissioner
Indiana Division of Labor
Indiana State Office Bldg.,
  Room 1012
100 North Senate Avenue
Indianapolis, Indiana 46204

Iowa
Jerry L. Addy, Commissioner
Bureau of Labor, State House
East 7th and Court Avenue
Des Moines, Iowa 50319

Kansas
Darrell D. Carlton,
  Commissioner
Department of Labor
401 Topeka Avenue
Topeka, Kansas 66603

Kentucky
William P. McElwain,
  Commissioner
Department of Health
275 East Main Street
Frankfort, Kentucky 40601

Louisiana
Division of State Planning
Office of the Governor
Baton Rouge, Louisiana

Maine
Miss Marion E. Martin,
Commissioner
Department of Labor and In-
dustry
State Labor Building
Augusta, Maine 04330
Wilbur Weeks, Director
Research and Statistics
Department of Labor and In-
dustry
Augusta, Maine 04330

Maryland
Henry Miller, Commissioner
Department of Labor and In-
dustry
State Office Building
301 West Preston Street
Baltimore, Maryland 21201

Massachusetts
Hervey Elkins, Director
Mass. Dept. of Labor and In-
dustries
Div. of Occupational Hygiene
39 Boyleston Street
Boston, Massachusetts 02116
Everett L. Grady, Director
Mass. Dept. of Labor and In-
dustries
Saltonstall State Office Bldg.
100 Cambridge Street
Boston, Massachusetts 02202

Michigan
Barry Brown, Director
Department of Labor
300 East Michigan Avenue
Lansing, Michigan 48933

Minnesota
E. I. Malone, Commissioner
Department of Labor and In-
dustry
110 State Office Building
St. Paul, Minnesota 55101

Mississippi
Dick B. Whitehead, Director
State Board of Health
Post Office Box 1700
Jackson, Mississippi 39205

Missouri
James J. Butler, Chairman
Industrial Commission
Department of Labor and In-
dustrial Relations
Box 599
Jefferson City, Missouri 65101

Montana
Roy Jameson, Director
Safety Department
Industrial Accident Board
Front and 14th Streets
Helena, Montana 59601
Benjamin Wake
Department of Health
Cogswell Building
State Capitol
Helena, Montana 59601
William A. Penttila
State Fire Marshal
State Capitol
Helena, Montana 59601

Nebraska
Gerald E. Chizek,
Commissioner
Department of Labor
State Capitol
Lincoln, Nebraska

Nevada

Ralph Langley
Department of Ind. Safety
Nevada Industrial Commission
515 East Musser Street
Carson City, Nevada 89701

New Hampshire

Robert M. Duvall,
    Commissioner
Department of Labor
State House Annex
Concord, New Hampshire 03301
Forrest H. Bumford, Director
Occupational Health Service
Division of Public Health Ser-
    vices
Department of Health and
    Welfare
61 South Spring Street
Concord, New Hampshire 03301
Richard Hawes, Director
Department of Centralized
    Data Processing
1 Pillsbury Street
Concord, New Hampshire 03301

New Jersey

Ronald M. Heyman,
    Commissioner
Department of Labor and In-
    dustry
John Fitch Plaza
Trenton, New Jersey 08625

New Mexico

Larry Gordon, Director
Environmental Services
Box 2348
Sante Fe, New Mexico 87501

New York

Louis L. Levine
Industrial Commissioner
Department of Labor
State Campus
Albany, New York 12226

North Carolina

Frank Crane, Commissioner
Department of Labor
P.O. Box 1151
Raleigh, N.C. 27602

North Dakota

Bronald Thompson, Chairman
Workmen's Compensation Bu-
    reau
State Capitol
Bismarck, North Dakota 58501

Ohio

Martin J. Hughes, Director
Department of Ind. Relations
220 Parsons Avenue
Columbus, Ohio 43215

Oklahoma

J. T. Weedman, Jr.
Administrative Assistant
Office of the Governor
State Capitol Building
Oklahoma City, Oklahoma
    73105
Dale McHard, Director
Occupational and Radiological
    Health Division
State Department of Health
3400 North Eastern
Oklahoma City, Oklahoma
    73105

Oregon

James R. Faulstich, Assistant
Economic Development and
Consumer Services
Office of the Governor
318 Public Service Building
Salem, Oregon 97310

Pennsylvania

Paul Smith, Secretary
Department of Labor and Industry
1700 Labor and Industry Bldg.
Harrisburg, Pennsylvania 17120
Dr. Maurice K. Goddard
Acting Secretary
Environmental Resources
519 South Office Building
Harrisburg, Pennsylvania 17120

Puerto Rico

Julia Rivera de Vincenti
Secretary of Labor
414 Barbosa Avenue
Hato Rey, Puerto Rico 00917

Rhode Island

Frank W. Marcaccio, Chief
Division of Industrial Inspection
Department of Labor
235 Promenade Street
Providence, Rhode Island 02903
Walter T. Dromgoole, Chief
Division of Statistics and Census
Department of Labor
235 Promenade Street
Providence, Rhode Island 02903

South Carolina

Edgar C. McGowan,
Commissioner
Department of Labor
Post Office Box 11329
Columbia, South Carolina 29211

South Dakota

Robert H. Hayes, M.D.
State Health Officer
State Department of Health
Pierre, South Dakota 57501

Tennessee

Leonard O. Evans
Commissioner
Tennessee Dept. of Labor
C1-130 Cordell Hull Bldg.
Nashville, Tennessee 37219
Eugene Fowinkle
Commissioner
Tennessee Department of
Public Health
344 Cordell Hull Building
Nashville, Tennessee 37219

Texas

Walter G. Martin, P.E.
Director
Division of Occupational Safety and State Safety Engineer
Texas Occupational Safety
Board
1100 West 29th Street
Austin, Texas 78756

Utah

Carlyle R. Gronning,
Chairman
Industrial Commission of Utah
Room 438, State Capitol
Salt Lake City, Utah 84114

Vermont
Louis Lavin, Commissioner
Department of Labor and Industry
Montpelier, Vermont 05602

Virgin Islands
Edmund L. Penn
Deputy Commissioner
Workmen's Compensation Division
Department of Labor
P.O. Box 708
Christiansted, St. Croix
Virgin Islands 00820

Virginia
Edmond P. Boggs,
  Commissioner
Department of Labor and Industry
Post Office Box 1814
Ninth Street Office Building
Richmond, Virginia 23214

Washington
William C. Jacobs, Director
Department of Labor and Industries
General Administration Building
Olympia, Washington 98501

West Virginia
John Ashcraft, Director
West Virginia Dept. of Mines
State Capitol
Charleston, West Virginia 25305

Fred L. Davis, Jr.,
  Commissioner
West Virginia Workmen's
  Compensation Fund
State Capitol
Charleston, West Virginia 25305

N. H. Dyer, Director
West Virginia Dept. of Health
State Capitol
Charleston, West Virginia 25305

Robert A. McConnell,
  Commissioner
West Virginia Department of
  Labor
State Capitol
Charleston, West Virginia 25305

Wisconsin

Philip E. Lerman,
  Director
Dept. of Industry, Labor and
  Human Resources
310 Price Place
Post Office Box 2209
Madison, Wisconsin 53701

Wyoming

William A. Cavanagh
State Safety Engineer
Occupational Health and Safety Commission
200 E. 8th Ave., P.O. Box 2186
Cheyenne, Wyoming 82001

PRIVATE ASSOCIATIONS CONCERNED WITH SAFETY AND HEALTH

The following is a list of private professional organizations whose activities affect the fields of safety and health.

American Association of Industrial Nurses
79 Madison Avenue
New York, New York 10016

American Conference of Governmental Industrial Hygienists
P.O. Box 1937
Cincinnati, Ohio 45301

American Industrial Hygiene Association
25711 Southfield Road
Southfield, Michigan 48075

American Insurance Alliance
85 John Street
New York, New York 10038

American Medical Association
Department of Environmental, Public, and Occupational Health
535 North Dearborn Street
Chicago, Illinois 60610

American Mutual Insurance Alliance
20 North Wacker Drive
Chicago, Illinois 60606

American National Standards Institute*
1430 Broadway
New York, New York 10018

American Society of Safety Engineers
850 Busse Highway
Park Ridge, Illinois 60068

Construction Safety Association
4750 North Sheridan Road
Chicago, Illinois 60640

Industrial Health Foundation, Incorporated
5321 Centre Avenue
Pittsburgh, Pennsylvania 15232

Industrial Medical Association
150 North Wacker Drive
Chicago, Illinois 60606

International Association of Government Labor Officials
7310 Woodward Avenue
Detroit, Michigan 48202

International Association of Industrial Accident Board and Commissions
150 Tremont Street
Boston, Massachusetts 02111

National Fire Protection Association*
60 Battery March Street
Boston, Massachusetts 02110

National Safety Council
425 North Michigan Avenue
Chicago, Illinois 60611

Unemployment Benefits Advisors, Incorporated
720 Hotel Washington
Washington, D.C. 20004

*A Congressionally-chartered organization for the development of consensus standards.

INDEX

This book was typeset by Demco, Inc. of Ann Arbor, Michigan,
and printed and bound by LithoCrafters, Inc. of Ann Arbor, Michigan.